THIRTY PLAYS
for
CLASSROOM READING

Thirty Plays

for

Classroom Reading

*A new approach to the reading program in the
Intermediate Grades*

by

DONALD D. DeWitt DURRELL

*Professor of Elementary Education,
Boston University*

and

B. ALICE CROSSLEY

*Associate Professor of Elementary Education,
Boston University*

Publishers   PLAYS, INC.   *Boston*

THIRTY PLAYS FOR CLASSROOM READING

Library of Congress Card Catalog Number: 57-6667

Reprinted 1960
Reprinted 1964
Reprinted 1966

Acknowledgments

The editors wish to acknowledge the help of many people in the preparation of THIRTY PLAYS FOR CLASSROOM READING. A. S. Burack, editor of PLAYS, The Drama Magazine for Young People, made available the richest possible supply of plays from the resources of the magazine. Mrs. Alice K. Nicholson, instructor in education at Boston University, was responsible for the tryout of many of the plays. We are grateful to the graduate students who conducted the research project which made an analytical evaluation of the plays: Ruth L. Bruce, Newell L. Jones, Justine E. Kenney, Janet H. Kilty, Camella M. Mondi, Doris B. Norton, Marilyn B. Reid, Eloise P. Seifert, and Myrtle M. Webb. The many teachers and pupils who assisted in the tryouts gave invaluable help.

CONTENTS

CONTENTS

Introduction

THIRTY PLAYS FOR CLASSROOM READING is designed to give new stimulus to the reading program and is planned as an essential part of the reading curriculum, not as a decorative "extra." The reading of plays adds many values to reading: it enlists the delight in dramatization which appears in the everyday make-believe of all children; it enriches imagery in the reading of fiction; it provides disciplines not found in other types of reading; it enhances comprehension, vocabulary development, phrase reading, and expression; it improves speech skills, and adds many personal and social values to the child's development. The zest play reading gives to classroom reading is especially important in the intermediate grades where study skills often become the sole objective in reading. The child in the intermediate grades is ready for the new approach to imaginative reading provided by THIRTY PLAYS FOR CLASSROOM READING.

The thirty plays in this book were selected from the hundreds of plays published by PLAYS, *The Drama Magazine for Young People*, the richest source of plays for children of all grades. Many plays were tried out in intermediate grade classrooms and were read and evaluated by more than five hundred children as a group research project at Boston University. The children rated the plays, indicated the characters they would most like to read, picked out the most interesting incidents, listed difficult words and phrases. The teachers also noted pupil reactions, growth in expression and reading skill, and evaluated the materials in each play. The plays most liked by children in grade four are presented here, but all plays were rated high by children in grades five and six. Both the selection of plays and the suggestions for study are the result of this tryout.

THIRTY PLAYS FOR CLASSROOM READING should be used as a regular part of the reading program. A set of five books is adequate for class needs, since the plays have a small number of characters and two children may use the same book. The preparation required is simple: the teacher (or a group of children) may decide on the parts to be read by different children; the sample lines at the beginning of the play are read to guide interpretation; the group of children retires to practice the reading; after this practice period the play is presented with children standing or sitting in a semicircle in front of the class. No staging or properties are needed. The narrator's part is written into the play and provides the necessary changes of scene.

Values in Play Reading

Imagination plays a large part in the lives of children. They have spent countless hours in imaginative play as mother, father, baby, doctor, nurse, teacher, policeman, robber, cowboy, Indian, sheriff, airplane pilot, spaceman, athlete, princess, king, or President. Their reveries include such dramatization even when they are not engaged in social play. Television, radio, movies, and books of fiction employ dramatization to catch the interests of millions of people.

The classroom teacher may use this force to enrich the reading program, increasing reading interests and adding to the importance of the reading skills program. All children enjoy the reading of plays; the dramatized situation is a familiar one to them—they have spent so many voluntary enjoyable hours in it. Play reading provides an outlet for the imagination.

Play Reading a Natural Bridge to the Reading of Fiction

Children who have not learned to enjoy the reading of fiction find play reading a natural bridge from imaginative play to imaginative reading. Most children enjoy having stories read to them, but some cannot find pleasure in reading to themselves. They can create vivid imagery while listening, getting "lost" in the seeming reality of the situation. In silent reading, however, some children fail to make these rich images and find reading dull. Yet these same children engage eagerly in dramatic play. Play reading combines the imagery-producing qualities of listening and self-dramatization. Play reading encourages imagery in reading, leading the child to the enjoyment of fiction and giving practice in translating words into images.

Social and Personal Values in Play Reading

Play reading is inherently sociable, with every person adding to the creation of the whole, and all enjoying the contributions of the others. The "social caste" system of a two- or three-level class is broken down; children at all reading levels may be cast in the same play, since each child learns to read his lines in the preparatory period. Undesirable competition is avoided, because every child reads a different part and each part is important to the whole play. A classroom becomes more closely knit socially when the pupils engage in mutual tasks that are enjoyed by everyone.

Undiscovered personality qualities are often brought out in play reading. When a child is "someone else" while reading a play, new and delightful aspects of his personality are often revealed. Plays are good for bringing out timid children, for finding sympathetic qualities in aggressive ones. By suitable casting, children can gain confidence in themselves and learn their own possibilities for improving social habits.

Plays allow discussion of personal qualities, manners, bad habits, and ethical choices without self-consciousness on the part of pupils or "moralizing" by the teacher. They can talk about the actions of the characters objectively, since the part they have taken is only imaginary.

Play reading requires disciplines not encountered in other reading. Alertness to timing of speeches, coming in at the right time, keeping one's place on the page, correct reading of words and phrases, good expression—these and other factors are recognized by the child as important to the success of the play. He cannot be inattentive or careless in his reading, or the desired effect is spoiled. Standards of craftsmanship in reading are important to him, and the voluntary disciplines he encounters in play reading help him in other situations.

Enhancing Reading Skills Through Play Reading

The motivating power of the true audience situation is always found in play reading. Comprehension is assured; the child cannot interpret his lines unless he understands them. Careless and inattentive reading is seldom encountered in play reading, because each child realizes the importance of his particular part; if he reads it inaccurately the listener is confused.

Attention to new words or unfamiliar phrases is equally important to interpretation of the lines of the play. While most of the words in the plays are within the oral vocabularies of children, there was no attempt to limit the words to the reading vocabulary of a particular level. As the child has the opportunity to learn the words in advance of presentation, and as no one part contains many difficult words, even the slower learner can read the parts successfully. Vocabulary enrichment is an essential part of play reading, and children enjoy displaying new words in the dramatized situation. Even the words of an unfamiliar period, words in dialect, or even parts in imperfect English are relished by children. If they are playing the parts of "stuffy" adults, they enjoy using very large words or stilted expressions.

Improvement of expression in reading, is, of course, the main outcome of play reading. Teachers who have used these plays comment favorably on the noticeable improvement in expression. The desire to read with good expression carries over into other reading. Superior silent reading does not assure good oral reading. Even pupils in advanced reading groups will profit by play reading, and the reluctant reader who resists descriptive or narrative passages, will take readily to reading dialogue.

Phrase reading is always improved by play reading. The child who is inclined to read a word at a time or to ignore commas and periods in oral reading, will strive voluntarily to make good phrases and to attend to punctuation when he reads plays.

Improving Speech Skills Through Play Reading

Because the listeners need to understand the play, poor enunciation and pronunciation are unacceptable in play reading. The child who is careless in speech habits finds that he *must* improve if people are to understand and enjoy his part in the play. The social pressure of one's classmates has greater effect than any amount of adult admonition.

The increase of oral vocabulary is a natural outcome of play reading. The child who has used new words to express ideas is more likely to venture into such words in his regular speech. Many expressions used in plays become a normal part of the child's speech pattern.

Values in Expressive Oral Reading

It is high time that oral reading resume some of its former importance in the reading program. The delights of much imaginative reading simply cannot be discovered by lonely silent reading. The increasing amount of oral reading in modern life requires that it be served in school. Almost every parent reads bedtime stories to children. More and more people appear before television and radio; there are frequent business and professional meetings at which papers are read; clubs and organizations in school and community life often require oral reading; almost anyone in an executive position finds some oral reading necessary. An inquiry among any group of adults will reveal that all would like to be better oral readers. Expressive oral reading should be given a significant place in the reading program, especially among children who will later have high responsibility.

Use of THIRTY PLAYS FOR CLASSROOM READING in Remedial Reading Classes.

Remedial reading is usually concerned with systematic development of basic reading skills. It requires carefully graded exercises in various vocabulary abilities, in comprehension and recall, in speeded skills and various thinking skills related to interpretation of reading. Although THIRTY PLAYS FOR CLASSROOM READING is not primarily a remedial reading book, it serves well some of the needs commonly found among children who have reading difficulty.

As the child approaches fourth grade reading ability, he will be able to get much enjoyment from THIRTY PLAYS FOR CLASSROOM READING. Even with somewhat lower reading ability, he can learn the lines of a particular part and share the pleasure of reading with others of higher reading ability. He may require several days of advance preparation, mastering his part and learning to follow the cues for his lines, but the reward for successful reading is highly motivating. Variety of reading is essential to high interest, and the preparation of a play for reading adds zest to the learning.

The reading of plays is especially helpful in phrase reading and for observing the importance of punctuation in reading. Word-by-word reading and awkward phrasing are helped by play reading. The analytical task of word perception is lightened by the reward of a meaningful sentence in a play. The poor reader is encouraged by successful handling of new vocabulary found in the lines of the play. He may need separate practice on words and phrases which appear in his part, but this is lightened by his anticipation of taking part in a play.

Since the burden of word learning often distracts the slow learner from the imagery contained in the reading material, the alternate listening and reading helps to keep the imagery alive. The child with reading difficulty often needs an unusual amount of help in preserving attention to imagery and meaning in reading. Plays help him greatly in both of these needs.

Values in the Content of the Plays

Although the values of play reading have been given much emphasis here, the plays themselves are desirable additions to the literature of the classroom. In content and spirit, they offer enrichment of ideas, aesthetics, literary values. Some are historical, some are highly imaginative, some nonsensical; many are humorous, some are regional, some present dialect—all reveal delightful aspects of character. The authors of the plays are experienced in writing plays for children. To keep a play moving, to bring out values in lines, to fit lines to normal speech patterns, and to write materials which appeal to children, requires particular experience and talent. Children's reactions to these plays reveal that the authors have accomplished their objectives well.

A study of the titles in the different sections of THIRTY PLAYS FOR CLASSROOM READING reveals the great variety of materials.

Suggestions to the Teacher

You are the key person in all reading instruction; certainly the delight which children find in *play reading* depends upon your interest and help. Although most children have spent many hours in imaginative play, many of them do not carry over their natural dramatic bents into oral reading. You will need to encourage some pupils to "get into their parts"—reading with feeling, adding small gestures, turning toward the person addressed, and changing the voice—pitch, rate, and quality—to get the most effective expression. While some children may be over-dramatic and tend to "burlesque" their lines, more will need help in bringing their parts to life.

Children will quickly learn that play reading requires constant alertness; each must follow all parts closely to be ready for his cue. Each must be ready to enter with his part even more quickly than he would in normal conversation; otherwise the play will lag. The snap and smartness of the dialogue contributes to a wide-awake listening audience. Few school situations require a more natural "self discipline" than play reading.

Use of the voice must be emphasized constantly. The voice imparts most of the meaning and feeling to the audience. With practice a child can make his voice express anger, surprise, excitement, fear, joy, mystery, annoyance, impatience and many other emotions. Emphasize the *feeling* to be imparted; it is the key to appropriate expression. Enunciation and clear diction are to be emphasized, although some children will tend to sacrifice them in the effort to read "naturally." But both dramatic effect and clarity in enunciation can be attained with practice; both are necessary for holding the audience.

When the cast has been chosen, the first thing for the pupils to do is to read the play silently to understand its meaning. Let them discuss the play among themselves, and prepare any questions they want to ask you about the play. When it is clear that they understand the play and they will have no difficulty with words or unfamiliar expressions, they should withdraw from the room to practice oral reading of the play. When they are ready, set a time for them to read to the class; this should usually be as soon as possible, since they will be eager to read. Specific suggestions for your use or the children's use appear in the introduction to each play. You should feel free to vary them as it seems best for the group.

Occasionally, it will be apparent to the teacher that the children's preparation for reading a play is inadequate; they are missing the fun of the play. If this is discovered after the play reading has begun, it is generally better to stop the reading with the statement that "you are not getting all of the fun out of this play, let's stop here and I will help you practice before you read it again." This has to be done without censure, since reluctant children cannot read a play well; the spirit of enjoyment always must be present. It is always a delicate decision to make, but expressionless reading kills enjoyment for both reader and listener. If only one or two children are failing to read their lines well, and they cannot be helped by your assistance on one or two lines, the decision to continue must rest on the total effect of the play. If the good readers can carry the play, it should continue. In any case, you must give assurance and confidence in the child's ultimate success in reading his part.

There are several ways to help children who have difficulty in expression. One is to make play reading a "class exercise" for one or two earlier plays. In the introduction to many of the plays, lines have been selected which may be used for this purpose. Write these on the blackboard, tell the class the feeling to be expressed, have several try the lines, select a good reading for a pattern, and have all of the children read it together with that expression. Choral reading of poetry will help, particularly if the poems chosen are full of expression, and require many types of change in speed, pitch, volume, and emotional content.

If a tape recorder is available, the group reading a play may record their reading in practice, play the tape back and criticize themselves. Or the entire play may be recorded on tape after the children are satisfied with their reading; then the recording may be played to the entire class, with the readers also being part of the audience. They can then participate in an evaluation period. Varied uses of the tape recorder may be one of the most valuable ways of improving the reading.

You will find many opportunities for increasing the value of play reading through adjusting to the social and emotional needs of your pupils. You will want to cast a play with children from several different reading levels. This is an unusual opportunity to mix the reading groups so that children may enjoy new companionships in reading. Poor readers may have the book several days in advance in order to memorize their lines, if necessary. Do not always assign them parts of minor characters with few lines if they are able to give good interpretations after they have mastered the reading. Children may be assigned parts which fit their natural bents, or they may be asked to read quite different types of characterization; often desirable hidden qualities will be discovered in this manner.

Make sure that everyone gets to read in plays frequently. If some children are left out of play reading through children's casting the plays, it will be a good idea for a "casting committee" to consult with you before they announce their decisions; this will give you a chance to call attention to the desirability of including children who need the pleasure of taking part.

Children will want to read some of these plays several times, changing the casting and finding new interpretations. Sometimes the whole class will want to hear these re-readings; at other times, a group of children will enjoy reading them again without an audience, just for their own pleasure.

Remember that the most important thing is to have fun with the reading of THIRTY PLAYS FOR CLASSROOM READING. If the delight is there, the other values will be present also!

The Plays

At the beginning of each play there is a series of activities to help prepare the children for the reading. These exercises include practices in use of voice, practices in cueing, suggestions for noticing punctuation, choral reading of unfamiliar phrases, patterns, glossaries for meanings of unfamiliar words and phrases and pronunciation keys for foreign names. These suggestions demand active participation and constant evaluation. Many of the lines used are taken from the plays themselves and will be met later during the reading.

The book is divided into three sections. In *Section One* the teacher works with the children all the time, directing the exercises, helping in the assignment of parts and directing the practice reading of the play.

In *Section Two* it is suggested that the teacher direct the preparation, remain with the children until parts have been assigned and leave them to practice by themselves under the leadership of a chairman.

In *Section Three* it is suggested that a chairman be appointed or elected, and the children follow the directions and prepare the play by themselves.

All of the plays contained in this book are designed for group activities. The number of characters in each play is listed at the beginning and the right number of each sex can be chosen and assigned to work together.

DONALD D. DURRELL

B. ALICE CROSSLEY

SECTION ONE

SECTION ONE

The Five Brothers

Read the play *The Five Brothers* to yourselves and be prepared to discuss these questions.

1. What did these brothers think of themselves?
2. What do you think the Stranger thought of them?
3. What is your opinion of the brothers?
4. What had they failed to do?

This is an easy play to read. It will be most important to keep alert and be sure you come in with the different parts on time.

There will be times when your voices will show

pride
fear
excitement
sadness
uncertainty

As you practice, see if you can find the parts described by the words above.

Read the play aloud together to practice.

Help one another with words, phrases, and voices.

After you have tried it once, talk it over and decide where you need to improve.

Sometime soon read the play to the rest of the class.

Let them tell you how they liked your reading and why.

THE FIVE BROTHERS

by Eleanore Leuser

Characters

(6 boys, and the narrator)

NARRATOR

THE FIVE BROTHERS, *simple, silly men who think they are very wise*

THE STRANGER, *much brighter than any of the brothers, helps them to settle their problem*

NARRATOR: Five brothers are riding across a bridge. They stop on the bridge and get off their horses to rest. Here is what they are saying.

1ST BROTHER: No one would ever take us for the Five Wisest Brothers of Salem.

2ND BROTHER: Ah, how wise we are!

3RD BROTHER: No one could be wiser!

4TH BROTHER: Not even our horses.

5TH BROTHER: We know everything.

1ST BROTHER: Shall we go over the bridge now that we have rested?

2ND BROTHER: I hate to mention it, Brother, but this bridge does not seem very safe.

3RD BROTHER: Oh, I feel it shaking!

4TH BROTHER: Oh, we shall all fall in the water!

5TH BROTHER: We shall all be drowned!

NARRATOR: They all climb on the backs of their horses but in their haste they fall over to the other side. They pick themselves up and get back on again. Let us listen to what they say now.

1ST BROTHER: Why, we're still on the bridge!

2ND BROTHER: We didn't fall in the water!

3RD BROTHER: The bridge is still standing!

4TH BROTHER: So are our horses!

5TH BROTHER: It is all the fault of our horses. They must have made us fall.

1ST BROTHER: Oh, my side aches!

2ND BROTHER: Oh, my leg!

3RD BROTHER: Oh, my head!

4TH BROTHER: I ache all over. But at least, my brothers, we are all together.

5TH BROTHER: But are we?

1ST BROTHER: We had better count. One of us might have fallen off the bridge.

5TH BROTHER: I will count, my brothers. One . . . two . . . three . . . four. There are only four! One of us *must* have fallen off the bridge.

1ST BROTHER: Oh, oh, no. . . . Here . . . I'll get off my horse. You get back on your horse and then let *me* count. There must be something wrong. One . . . two . . . three . . . four. Alas! Alas! There are only four. One of us must have fallen off the bridge!

2ND BROTHER: Wait! You must be wrong. I'll get down. You get back on your horse and then let *me* count. One . . . two . . . three . . . four. Oh, dear, I did no better.

NARRATOR: As they talk about what to do, a stranger approaches and speaks to them.

STRANGER: My good men, whatever is the matter?

2ND BROTHER: We are the Five Wisest Brothers of Salem and one of us has just fallen off the bridge and been drowned.

STRANGER: The *Five* Wisest Brothers, you say? That's queer! How do you know one of you fell off the bridge and was drowned?

3RD BROTHER: We counted and there are only four.

STRANGER: Are you sure? Let me see one of you count.

4TH BROTHER: I will gladly . . . if my brothers will stay on their horses. One . . . two . . . three . . . four. See, there are only four!

STRANGER: Ha, ha, ha, ha, ha. That's the funniest thing I ever heard.

5TH BROTHER: You should not laugh at our misfortune.

STRANGER: Forgive me. But I think I can help you to find your fifth brother.

1ST BROTHER: Wonderful! Where?

2ND BROTHER: Where?

3RD BROTHER: If you can find him we will give you a purse of gold.

4TH BROTHER: Yes, a big purse!

STRANGER: Now, all get on your horses quickly and listen to me count you. One . . . two . . . three . . . four . . . five. THERE! There is your fifth brother!

5TH BROTHER: Wonderful! Wonderful!

1ST BROTHER: Wonderful! Yes, now we are five!

3RD BROTHER: Here is the purse of gold.

STRANGER: No, keep it and give it to the first ones you find more foolish than you. I must be off.

1ST BROTHER: Now what did he mean by that, my brothers?

4TH BROTHER: He is just very foolish and we are very wise!

1ST BROTHER: Yes, we are the Five Wisest Brothers of Salem!

THE END

Ben Franklin, Peace-Maker

In this play it is important to use your voice to show exactly how you feel.

Say this line as if you were excited and a little out of breath:

"Ben! Ben! I just saw Mrs. Cross coming this way, muttering and waving a stick."

Have someone try this line. The voice should be cross and sputtering:

"I'll find that John and give him a piece of my mind and a piece of my stick, too! Cheating an honest body! That's what he tried to do. But I'll tell his father."

Use a quiet, courteous tone when you say this line:

"Why he left, Mrs. Cross. Father needed me to help here in the shop, so I'm not going to school any more."

Let different boys and girls try the lines above. Help each other to improve the reading.

Now you are ready to choose people for the different parts. Practice reading together.

If you have the part of Mrs. Cross, *be cross* and show it.

If you are Ben, be quiet and polite.

Speak clearly and distinctly.

Come in with your parts promptly.

Try the play two or three times until you feel you are ready to read it for others.

BEN FRANKLIN, PEACE-MAKER

by Helen L. Howard

Characters

(2 boys, 1 man, 1 woman, and the narrator)

NARRATOR

BEN FRANKLIN, *age ten—a bright boy who keeps his temper and his wits when others get angry*

NATHAN, *Ben's friend*

MR. FRANKLIN, *Ben's father*

MRS. CROSS, *a very angry woman who is sure she has been cheated and means to make trouble*

NARRATOR: A long time ago, 1716, to be exact, when Benjamin Franklin was ten years old, he worked in his father's candle and soap shop on Union Street in Boston. As the play opens, Mrs. Cross is hurrying toward the shop. She is very angry. She is carrying a black bag and a stick. Listen!

MRS. CROSS: I'll find that John and give him a piece of my mind and a piece of my stick, too! Now, where has that sign gone? The blue ball with "Josiah Franklin" on it! I'll be bound they've taken it down. Don't want honest folks to find their way back! It must be near here some place. Cheating an honest body! That's what he tried to do. But I'll tell his father. This Union Street is so narrow and crooked a body almost meets herself going down the street. Oh, there's the shop. I'll just go right in and face him, that's what I'll do!

NARRATOR: Over in the shop we find Ben. Nathan, his friend, comes in. He is all out of breath.

NATHAN: Ben! Ben! I just saw Mrs. Cross coming this way, muttering and waving a stick. I heard her saying she was looking for the sign of the Blue Ball, so she must be coming here!

BEN: I wonder what's the matter.

NATHAN: I don't know. I couldn't understand what she said, but you'd better look out. She might hit you with that stick! She's very angry!

BEN: Thanks, Nat, for warning me. I'll just step back in the other room and wait for her. Maybe she'll cool down a little if she doesn't see anyone for just a minute.

NATHAN: Good luck! I'd better leave now.

NARRATOR: Ben goes to the back room of the shop. A moment later Mrs. Cross comes into the shop and looks around.

MRS. CROSS: Humph! He's hiding! John! John Franklin! You come right out here and face me! I won't be cheated! I won't stand for it. John! John, do you hear me?

BEN: Why, good morning, Mrs. Cross.

MRS. CROSS: It's you, is it, Ben? What are you doing here? Why aren't you in school?

BEN: I'm not going to school any more, Mrs. Cross.

MRS. CROSS: Expelled, I suppose. Some devilment, I'll be bound. You're just like your brother John. Where is he?

BEN: Why John left, Mrs. Cross. Father needed me to help here in the shop, so I'm not going to school any more.

MRS. CROSS: John's gone? Where did he go? Ran away, I suppose.

BEN: No, ma'am. John's gone into business for himself. He has a soap and candle shop of his own, over in New Jersey.

MRS. CROSS: Well, he won't get very far, cheating folks the way he does. Look at this cake of soap with a whole corner gone. I paid for a whole cake, and I didn't get it!

BEN: Well, there is quite a chunk missing, ma'am. It looks as if it had been broken off. Could you have had something heavy in your bag the day you carried the soap home?

MRS. CROSS: Well, yes. I did have an iron candleholder in my bag. But you needn't try to fix it up that way. The soap isn't in my bag. I looked before I came. Here I'll just turn the bag upside-down and shake it. . . . Why, there it is. Now, how can that be! I didn't see it before.

BEN: It may have been stuck in the lining, Mrs. Cross. But it has caused you time and trouble, so I'm going to give you an extra bar of soap.

MRS. CROSS: Why, thank you, Ben. I'm glad your brother didn't cheat me after all.

BEN: Father will be glad that you came to see about it.

MRS. CROSS: I'm glad I came, too. And, Ben, I'm real sorry you had to leave school. Folks say you are real smart and were learning a lot at school. The schoolmaster said that some day we'd all be hearing a lot about you and that you'd be a famous man.

BEN: I reckon I won't be famous, Mrs. Cross, but I do like to learn about things.

NARRATOR: At this moment Ben's father enters the store and greets Mrs. Cross.

MR. FRANKLIN: Good morning, Mrs. Cross.

MRS. CROSS: Good morning, Josiah Franklin. I'm just getting acquainted with Ben. He's that smart already! I expect he'll be a great statesman one of these days.

MR. FRANKLIN: I don't know about that, Mrs. Cross, but he does like to experiment with all sorts of things. He learns about everything he sees.

MRS. CROSS: Mark my word. He'll be a great peace-maker, as well as a great inventor one of these days.

THE END

The Lion and the Mouse

The Lion and the Mouse is an old, old story that you have heard many times before. This play is written in a different way from the old story. It is really written in rhyme. If you are not very careful when you read it, you will make it sound sing-song and it will not be interesting to listen to.

First try working on some of the parts of the play.

Read these phrases to yourself. The words are not difficult but some of them are put together in an unusual way.

a great and wonderful beast
I meant you no harm
feel no alarm
you've plenty of pluck
don't begin bragging
the last stake is driven
he's really a prize
alas, this day is an unhappy one
oh, woe is me
he's vanished, all right
there's surely no doubt
full of anger and spite

Now take turns reading these phrases aloud. Read smoothly and without stopping between words.

Read this line as if you were the Mouse talking to the Lion. Put *fear* into your voice:

"I meant you no harm."

Read the next line as if you were the Lion. Make your voice *strong* and *powerful:*

"Feel no alarm. You've plenty of pluck."

Read the next line as you think the Lion would say it after he is caught in the net:

"Alas, this day is an unhappy one. Oh, woe is me!"

Choose five boys to be hunters. See how quickly you can come in with your parts. Make your voices excited and bragging.

1ST HUNTER: We've got him! We've got him! He's tight in the net!

2ND HUNTER: Don't begin *bragging.* He isn't safe yet!

3RD HUNTER: Hurry! Be quick now!

4TH HUNTER: He's certainly *strong.*

3RD HUNTER: There! The last stake is driven. Now what can go wrong?

2ND HUNTER: Just look at his *size!*

1ST HUNTER: And look at that *mane!*

4TH HUNTER: He's *really* a *prize!*

With the help of your teacher choose someone for every part in the play.

Read your part carefully to yourself. Ask for help on words you do not know. Watch the periods and commas.

Practice reading the play together. Remember to:

1. Use your voice to make the play seem real.
2. Be ready to come in with your part right on time.
3. Help each other when you need to.

Arrange to read the play to the class sometime soon.

THE LION AND THE MOUSE

adapted by June Barr

Characters

(7 boys, and a narrator)

NARRATOR

THE LION, *is just what he should be; a big strong animal who thinks of himself as King of the Forest*

THE MOUSE, *is just a mouse. He is tiny but smart and helps the Lion out of difficulty*

FIVE HUNTERS, *five bragging men who finally quarrel with each other*

NARRATOR: The Lion is asleep in the clearing in the forest. The Mouse comes running in. He stops to sniff the air and look for danger. He sees the Lion, and goes close to admire the big animal.

MOUSE: My! What a great and wonderful beast! He must be the King of the Forest, at least.

LION: Arrummph! Mmmph! And who might you be? Don't you know better than to fool with me? You're just the right size for me to eat. And you know, you might taste very sweet!

MOUSE: Oh, King of the Forest, please let me go! I meant you no harm, and how do we know, some day I may be able to help *you.*

LION: Ha, ha, ha, ha. *You* help *me?* What could *you* do?

MOUSE: I might do *something*, and I meant you no harm. . . .

LION: All right, I won't eat you . . . feel no alarm.

MOUSE: Thank you, King Lion, I wish you good luck!

LION: I wish you the same, for you've plenty of pluck!

NARRATOR: And so the Lion starts slowly away. Suddenly five hunters appear. They run quietly up behind the Lion and throw a net over him. The Lion struggles and roars. The hunters talk excitedly.

1ST HUNTER: We've got him! We've got him! He's tight in the net!

2ND HUNTER: Don't begin bragging. He isn't safe yet!

3RD HUNTER: Hurry! Be quick now!

4TH HUNTER: He's certainly strong!

3RD HUNTER: There! The last stake is driven! Now what can go wrong?

5TH HUNTER: You never can tell. . . .

4TH HUNTER: He can't break away.

2ND HUNTER: We've got him at last!

1ST HUNTER: What a lucky day!

3RD HUNTER: Isn't he wonderful?

2ND HUNTER: Just look at his size!

1ST HUNTER: And look at that mane!

4TH HUNTER: He's really a prize!

5TH HUNTER: He's the finest lion I've seen in an age.

3RD HUNTER: Shall we go back to the village and get a cage?

5TH HUNTER: Yes, we'll cage him and take him back to the King.

4TH HUNTER: What a present!

3RD HUNTER: The best any loyal subject could bring.

4TH HUNTER: We're sure to receive a reward for our pains.

1ST HUNTER: And remember, we all share alike in the gains!

2ND HUNTER: Shall I stay and guard him?

1ST HUNTER: Oh, he'll be all right!

3RD HUNTER: He's safe in the net.

4TH HUNTER: And it's fastened down tight!

2ND HUNTER: Let's go get the cage, then.

NARRATOR: The hunters have left. The Mouse has been watching them from his hiding place. He now comes out and approaches the Lion. The Lion speaks to the Mouse.

LION: Oh, little Mouse, did you see what they've done? Alas, this day is an unhappy one! They'll carry me away in a cage and then I shall never see my dear forest again!

MOUSE: Now, wait just a minute. . . .

LION: Oh, woe is me!

MOUSE: Oh, King of the Forest, I can set you free!

LION: What can a mouse do? No, it's too late.

MOUSE: Now, you just be patient, please, and wait. . . . Let me gnaw the rope. . . . There. That rope is free.

LION: That's nice, but what good can one rope do?

MOUSE: Now just you wait, and I'll gnaw them *all* through!

LION: Oh, hurry, hurry, they'll be back any minute!

MOUSE: They'll find an empty net, with no lion in it!

LION: Oh, I believe you can do it! Oh, hurry, please!

MOUSE: Of course I can do it! . . . I'll gnaw these . . . and these. . . .

LION: I'm free! You've done it! You've set me free! And I thought you were too small to do anything for *me!*

MOUSE: I told you I'd repay. . . .

LION: Yes, I guess in the end a *little* friend is often the *greatest* friend!

MOUSE: Listen! The hunters!

LION: They're close to us, too! Let us hide in the brush and see what they'll do!

NARRATOR: The Lion and the Mouse hide in the brush and watch the hunters come into the clearing with a large cage on poles. They set it down and look for the Lion. The hunters talk together as they move about.

1ST HUNTER: He's gone!

2ND HUNTER: Oh, he can't be!

3RD HUNTER: We tied him down tight!

4TH HUNTER: He couldn't get loose!

5TH HUNTER: Well, he's vanished, all right!

1ST HUNTER: The stakes are in place.

2ND HUNTER: But these ropes are gnawed through!

3RD HUNTER: A lion can't gnaw rope!

4TH HUNTER: Someone helped him.

5TH HUNTER: That must be true.

1ST HUNTER: Well, he's gone, and that's that.

THE LION AND THE MOUSE 15

3RD HUNTER: Who will tell our great King?

4TH HUNTER: You would go and brag of the great beast we'd bring.

1ST HUNTER: And now the King's waiting.

2ND HUNTER: How angry he'll be!

5TH HUNTER: When I wanted to tell him, you were quick to agree!

4TH HUNTER: You made us excited!

3RD HUNTER: And now the lion's escaped!

2ND HUNTER: Well, I'm not to blame, for I offered to stay!

3RD HUNTER: You're in this with us.

1ST HUNTER: You just can't back out!

2ND HUNTER: Oh, yes I can! Goodbye!

5TH HUNTER: And there's surely no doubt that I shall go too, for you are unfair.

4TH HUNTER: Come back!

1ST HUNTER: You'll pay for this!

3RD HUNTER: If you leave us, beware!

4TH HUNTER: They've gone. And now, who'll tell our King?

3RD HUNTER: Yes, who's going to tell him . . . that is the thing.

4TH HUNTER: It ought to be you, for you bragged more than I.

1ST HUNTER: No, it ought to be you!

3RD HUNTER: Me? Why me?

4TH HUNTER: Well, someone must tell him.

3RD HUNTER: That much is true.

1ST HUNTER: It ought to be you!

4TH HUNTER: No, it ought to be you!

NARRATOR: They are still arguing as they go out of the forest. The Lion and the Mouse come from their hiding place. The Mouse looks around.

MOUSE: Are they gone?

LION: Yes, they're gone, full of anger and spite.

MOUSE: They didn't stick together . . . it just doesn't seem right! Now their friendship is broken and never will mend!

LION: Well, we'll stick together! Come along, little friend.

There's a part of this forest so deep and so green, a place where the hunters never are seen. We'll go there to-gether. . . .

MOUSE: What good friends we'll be!

LION: Yes, I will help you, and you can help me!

THE END

Turncoat

Read the play to yourself. Think about these questions as you read.

What two countries were at war?

To what country did the Duke really belong?

What was peculiar about the Duke's new coat?

The word "turncoat" has two meanings in this story. Discuss the meaning of the word as it is used in the title of this play.

What is your feeling about the Duke?

There are a few words and phrases in this play that may be difficult to understand. Go over them now.

medieval castle—a very old castle built in the middle ages

the cause is a righteous one—the reason for fighting is right and fair

within the castle—inside the castle

treaty-breakers—people who do not keep faith with a written agreement

closeted with his tailor—in the room with his tailor

renders me safe—keeps me safe

discretion, Nephew, discretion—take care, be cautious

we shan't be molested—shall not be bothered, disturbed, injured

put to flight—caused to run away

The most important thing in this play will be the job of reading your part smoothly and with meaning. This will be particularly true because the people in the play use a type of speech which is different from that we use today.

Try a few lines from the play to see how well you can read the parts. Choose a boy and girl to try these sentences:

DUCHESS: *Henri!* Where have you *been* all morning, Nephew?

NEPHEW: Riding. The French army is approaching! Where's my uncle?

DUCHESS: The Duke is within the castle. . . . He has been closeted with his tailor all morning.

NEPHEW: Again? He must be having a new uniform made.

Now let two others try the lines. Decide how well you read by answering these questions.

Did we sound like people talking together?
Could every word be heard?
Did we use our voices to show different feelings?

With the help of your teacher choose parts in the play.

Read the play together several times. Help each other when needed. When you are ready, tell the teacher and arrange to read the play to the entire class.

TURNCOAT

by Bernard J. Reines

Characters

(2 women, 5 men, and the narrator)

NARRATOR

DUCHESS, *fearful of war but does as her husband suggests*

HONORÉ, *a young girl who serves the Duchess*

NEPHEW, *a loyal Frenchman who is surprised and disgusted with his uncle, the Duke*

DUKE, *a middle-aged man*

TAILOR, *an older man who made the Duke's new coat*

SPANISH CAPTAIN, *the leader of the Spanish forces*

FRENCH CAPTAIN, *the leader of the French forces*

NARRATOR: Our play today takes us back many years to an old medieval castle in southern France. Just outside the castle we find the Duchess and Honoré, her attendant. The Duchess is shaking her head sadly as she speaks.

DUCHESS: War between France and Spain. . . . There will be much bloodshed, Honoré.

HONORÉ: Yes, Duchess. But the cause of France is a righteous one. We are in honor bound to fight!

DUCHESS: I know, I know . . . but now my husband and my only nephew will be off to the war. . . . The good Lord will guard the right. Come, Honoré, let us go within.

HONORÉ: But here is your nephew, Duchess.

NEPHEW: Duchess!

DUCHESS: Henri! Where have you been all morning, Nephew?

NEPHEW: Riding. The French army is approaching! Where's my uncle?

DUCHESS: The Duke is within the castle.

NEPHEW: Finishing his preparations. . . . We'll show those Spanish treaty-breakers!

HONORÉ: The Duke has been closeted with his tailor all morning.

NEPHEW: Again? He must be having a new uniform made. I'll go to him.

NARRATOR: As the nephew is about to leave the Duke enters, followed by his tailor. The tailor is hastily sewing the last few stitches in a blue jacket worn by the Duke. The tailor finishes, cuts the thread, steps back, and bows low.

TAILOR: There, Sire. It is finished.

DUKE: It is most becoming, is it not?

TAILOR: Indeed it is, Sire. But with your splendid figure. . . .

DUKE: Thank you. Thank you. Now, run along. My dear Duchess, it is most becoming, don't you think?

DUCHESS: Yes.

NEPHEW: Is that . . . is that a new style in uniforms, Uncle?

DUKE: What? A new style . . . ? You have guessed it, Henri.

This is a uniform that renders me safe under all circumstances.

NEPHEW: It doesn't look that wonderful. . . . Uncle, the French army is almost here! We can join them today.

DUKE: Really? You're an impatient lad, aren't you?

NEPHEW: But Uncle. . . . Look! The army of France! Good day, Captain.

FRENCH CAPTAIN: Halt! I greet you in the name of His Majesty, the King of France!

DUKE: In the name of His Majesty, the King of France!

FRENCH CAPTAIN: We are about to engage the army of Spain, which is drawn up for battle just over that hill. Since you are a loyal subject of the King of France, I ask you to join us, with your men, at once.

DUKE: Nothing would give me greater joy. But unfortunately . . . some little time must pass before I can answer the call of duty and honor. It happens my preparations are not quite complete. And soldiers without proper arms and armor are of little use in battle. However, I shall lead my men to you at the earliest possible moment. . . . Meantime, tell His Majesty . . . I wear his colors!

FRENCH CAPTAIN: I shall tell him. He will expect you and your men soon.

DUKE: In the name of France!

FRENCH CAPTAIN: In the name of France!

NARRATOR: The Captain takes his place between his men. They march off at the head of the army. The Duke turns to speak.

DUKE: Well . . . I must say, I handled that well.

NEPHEW: But, Uncle . . . what further preparations must we make? Our men are fully equipped.

DUKE: Discretion, Nephew, discretion. How do I know that the army of France will win? How do I know that the King of France will reward me adequately?

NEPHEW: Uncle! But our duty . . . our honor. . . .

DUKE: Words . . . mere words. What if Spain proves the stronger . . . offers me more?

NEPHEW: It would still be our duty to fight for our country . . . for France!

DUKE: Silence! We shall soon know. Henri, take your horse and ride to the field of battle. As soon as the outcome is clear, return and tell me who has won.

NEPHEW: Yes, Uncle. I shall do your bidding.

DUKE: And now, my dear Duchess . . . let us go in and enjoy some music.

DUCHESS: My lord, what if the Spanish army wins! They will know you for an enemy.

DUKE: Leave that to me, my dear. Come, let us take our pleasure.

NARRATOR: The women start towards the door. The Duke follows. Here comes the Nephew. He is breathless.

NEPHEW: Uncle! The French. . . .

DUKE: Yes, Henri? The French?

NEPHEW: Are defeated! They are retreating. The Spanish are sweeping forward!

DUKE: Really?

DUCHESS: What shall we do? We are lost!

NEPHEW: Not at all. We can withdraw with the French army. Or we can hold the castle. The Spaniards can't stop now to lay siege to us . . . and they may be defeated in the next battle.

DUKE: We shan't be molested. Give me a hand, Henri. Help me off with my coat. As a matter of fact, I've been thinking of going over to the Spaniards for some time now. Their king is richer. . . . Ah, do I hear them?

NEPHEW: The Spaniards!

DUKE: Help me turn this coat! Quickly! Now help me into it, Henri. . . . There!

NEPHEW: The coat . . . the color!

DUCHESS: Here they come! Here is the Spanish Captain!

SPANISH CAPTAIN: In the name of His Majesty, the King of Spain!

DUKE: In the name of His Majesty, the King of Spain!

SPANISH CAPTAIN: The glorious army of Spain has put to flight the forces of France. But one victory does not mean we have won the war. Since you are a loyal subject of the King of Spain, I ask you to join us with your men at once, so that we may press forward even stronger to increase our advantage.

DUKE: His Majesty rewards his loyal subjects richly, does he not?

SPANISH CAPTAIN: Most richly.

DUKE: Ah, yes. Nothing would give me greater joy. But unfortunately, some little time must pass before I can answer the call of duty and honor. It happens my preparations are not quite complete. And soldiers without proper arms and armor are of little use in battle. . . . However, I shall rush my men to you at the earliest possible moment. . . . Meantime, tell His Majesty. . . . I wear *his* colors!

SPANISH CAPTAIN: In the name of Spain!

DUKE: In the name of Spain!

NEPHEW: Turncoat! . . . TURNCOAT!

THE END

Thankful Indeed

Thankful Indeed is an old tale. The words in it are not diffi-cult. The parts are not difficult. If you can come in quickly and keep the play moving along, you will do well.

This play, too, has many lines that rhyme. If you are not very careful it will become sing-song and lose its meaning.

Let us practice changing this line by emphasizing different words.

> Thank you indeed, for I was in *need*.
> *Thank* you indeed, for I was in need.
> Thank you *indeed*, for I was in need.
> Thank you indeed, for *I* was in need.
> Thank you *indeed*, for *I* was in *need*.

The above lines are in the story many times in different parts. Each person may read them in the way he thinks best for his part.

Now try this line:

> I am troubled *indeed*. I've not what I need.
> I am *troubled* indeed. I've not what I need.
> I am troubled indeed. I've not what I *need*.
> I am troubled *indeed*. *I've* not what I need.

Choose people for the parts in the play. Read your part to yourself. Ask for any help you need.

Practice the play together. Before you decide you have fin-ished your practice, be sure you can say *yes* to the following:

> We are not reading too rapidly.
> All voices are clear. Every word can be heard and under-stood.

We sound as if we are real people talking together.

We are not reading in a sing-song fashion.

We are ready to come in with our parts every time.

Plan with your teacher about reading to the rest of the class.

THANKFUL INDEED

by *Helen L. Howard*

Characters

(1 boy, 4 men, and the narrator)

NARRATOR

BOB, *a kind boy who tries to help many people. He wants a pumpkin very much.*

THE BUTCHER, *who is trying to find fresh eggs*

THE BLACKSMITH, *who is trying to get a new coat*

THE TAILOR, *who wants some sausage*

THE FARMER, *who needs a shoe for his horse*

NARRATOR: Bob is walking along the highway carrying some eggs in a basket.

BOB: There are no pumpkins at the market. I am so sorry to disappoint my mother. We did so want a pumpkin pie for our dinner. I shall take the eggs home again. Oh, hello, Butcher.

BUTCHER: Hello, young man.

BOB: Why are you looking so unhappy?

BUTCHER: I am troubled indeed. I've not what I need. My little son is ill and needs some fresh eggs.

BOB: I have some eggs. I am glad indeed! I have what you need.

BUTCHER: I shall be so glad to give you some sausage for the eggs.

BOB: You may have the eggs. I wanted a pumpkin but I will trade with you.

BUTCHER: Thank you indeed, for I was in need.

BOB: Mother cannot make a pie of sausage, but she will be glad that I helped the Butcher. Here comes the Tailor.

TAILOR: Hello, young man.

BOB: Hello, Tailor.

TAILOR: I am troubled indeed. I've not what I need.

BOB: What do you need? Perhaps I can help you.

TAILOR: I want some sausage. There is no better seasoning than sausage.

BOB: I have some sausage. I am glad indeed. I have what you need.

TAILOR: I shall be glad to give you this fine piece of cloth for the sausage.

BOB: You may have the sausage. I wanted a pumpkin but I will trade with you.

TAILOR: Thank you indeed, for I was in need.

BOB: Mother cannot make a pie of cloth, but she will be glad that I helped the Tailor. Oh, hello, Blacksmith.

BLACKSMITH: I am troubled indeed. I've not what I need.

BOB: Did I hear you say that you are in need?

BLACKSMITH: Yes. I need a new coat badly. If I had a piece of cloth, my wife could make a coat for me. But no cloth could I find in the market place, even though I am willing to give this fine horseshoe in exchange.

BOB: I have some cloth. I am glad indeed. I have what you need. I'll trade this cloth for your horseshoe.

BLACKSMITH: I am thankful indeed, to get what I need. Thank you very much. I must hurry to my wife.

BOB: My mother cannot make a pie of the horseshoe, but she will be glad that I helped the Blacksmith. I may as well go home even if I haven't what I need. . . . Hello, Farmer.

FARMER: Hello, Bob. I am troubled indeed. I have not what I need.

BOB: Why does your pony move so slowly?

FARMER: My little pony has lost his shoe. I am on my way to

market with a very big load, and my little pony can hardly go any farther.

BOB: I am glad indeed. I have what you need. Here is a horse-shoe, Mr. Farmer.

FARMER: The very thing I need. Now my little pony can pull the cart to market. I was so afraid that many people might be disappointed if I didn't get to market today. See what I have in my cart. I have a whole cart-load of pumpkins. Here is the finest one for you. I am thankful indeed to get what I need.

BOB: A pumpkin is exactly what I need! Thank you, Mr. Farmer. Now my mother can make a pumpkin pie. By helping others I got what I needed. I am thankful indeed, I have what I need.

THE END

In the Days of King Alfred

This play takes place hundreds of years ago when the Danes were trying to invade England. In those days people spoke in a very different way from the way we do. If you practice, you can make these speeches sound as they should.

First study a few words that may be difficult.

the rallying place—the gathering place
leather tunic—a long blouse made of leather
my strength is spent—I am very tired, all worn out
the men are massing—the men are gathering
how did he bear himself—how did he stand and act
naught else—nothing else
vagabond—a lazy person who wanders about, a tramp
crock—pottery jar

Here are some of the difficult lines from the play. Study them for a few minutes. Then try reading them together with the teacher. Keep reading together many times until you feel confident. Be very careful to pause at periods and commas:

"Close by, at the forest's edge, our men are gathering. *All* are listening for King Alfred's *horn*. *Once* we hear that, we'll know the *rallying* place."

"Pardon, good dame. My *strength* is *spent*."

"All day I've fought *briars* through the woods and *roots* through the swamps. To be *lost* in this forest did me more hurt than any *Dane* had managed."

"Leaves in a high *wind* could not have sped more quickly."

"Can scattered leaves go back and be a *grove?* A grove of oaks that will not *bend,* nor *break?*"

"Away with you! I will not help a man so stupid! Not if he were the King himself. Burned! You blockhead! You numskull! You stupid vagabond!"

"When men who're no account go free, why not the King instead?"

"But Joan, the vagabond you told me of, whom you sent on but now. What did he look like?"

"Why, ragged he was, with bleeding face, and grime. Yet, now I do recall. Hung from his shoulder was a mighty horn."

Choose people for the parts.

Read the parts aloud. Help each other with difficult words, voices and punctuation.

Are you ready to read for the other children?

IN THE DAYS OF KING ALFRED

by Ruth Vickery Holmes

Characters

(2 men, 1 woman, and the narrator)

NARRATOR

FULKE, *a woodcutter, who is fighting for England*

JOAN, *his wife, who is worried for fear that England will be lost. She is a quick, impatient woman.*

KING ALFRED, *a worried king. His soldiers ran from battle and he is fearful that he will not be able to get them together again.*

NARRATOR: Let us go back many years ago to the days of one of England's kings, King Alfred. The King and his men were fighting the Danes who were trying to invade England.

During one of the battles we find Fulke, a woodcutter who is a very loyal Englishman, coming back to his wife, Joan, at their little cottage in the woods.

FULKE: Quick, Joan, quick. Unbar the door.

JOAN: Oh, Fulke. You're home. And safe. Are the Danes driven back?

FULKE: No. They've driven us back. All King Alfred's force is scattered far and wide.

JOAN: But the King? Was King Alfred taken?

FULKE: That's as may be. Nobody knows. It was each man for himself. These woods are full of Englishmen in hiding. The Danes don't like to leave the open country.

JOAN: Where will the King make a stand again?

FULKE: No one knows where that will be. But close by, at the forest's edge, our men are gathering. And all are listening for King Alfred's horn. Once we hear that, we'll know the rallying place. I must be off to join them.

JOAN: But you need food. See, there's still a little meal. If you will wait, I'll make a batch of cakes.

FULKE: No. No, I must be off. Have the cakes ready. I'll come later if I can. But I must join the other men straight away, and listen for the sound of the King's horn.

JOAN: Pray God you hear it. Pray God the King is safe.

NARRATOR: Just as Fulke is out of sight, a man peers in the window of the cottage. This man looks tired and dirty. His face and hands are badly scratched. His long, dark green cape is tattered and torn. As he moves to get a better look into the cottage, a hunting horn can be seen hanging over his leather tunic. He is about to speak.

KING ALFRED: Pardon, good dame. My strength is spent. I am seeking food and lodging.

JOAN: Oh . . . but you startled me. Your clothes are torn, and there is blood upon your face.

KING ALFRED: All day I've fought briars through the woods, and roots through the swamps. To be lost in this forest did me more hurt than any Dane had managed.

JOAN: Then you were at the battle? You are one of the King's men?

KING ALFRED: One of England's men . . . but as for the battle . . . it was hardly a battle. The Danes broke through our lines. All our forces scattered. Leaves in a high wind could not have sped more quickly.

JOAN: But what of King Alfred? Have you news of him?

KING ALFRED: The King was cut off from his men. There was nothing he could do but flee. And flee he did. No one knows where.

JOAN: Ah, thank God the King escaped. Given more time, he *will* drive back the Danes.

KING ALFRED: Defeated, lost, alone . . . how can the King drive back the Danes?

JOAN: That's for the King to say. Lost he may be, and all his forces scattered. But when the King's horn sounds, his men will find him. There'll be a rallying place, then a new army.

KING ALFRED: Are you sure of that? Can scattered leaves go back and be a grove, a grove of oaks that will not bend, nor break?

JOAN: Your words are hard for me to follow. But if you are asking me whether the King will rally a new army, that I *know*. Already men are waiting at the forest's edge. They only need to find their King. They will fight again.

KING ALFRED: I asked for food. But your words are doing more for me than food. I'll go on my way.

JOAN: No, a bite to eat before you go. See, these cakes are nearly ready. If you will watch them, I will milk the cow. I will unbar the door. Come in.

KING ALFRED: Ah, something to eat will be most welcome.

JOAN: Mind how you watch the cakes. They're from the very last meal in my meal crock. *Do not let them burn!*

NARRATOR: Joan leaves and the man looks at the cakes. He then turns and walks up and down the little room talking to himself. Let's listen to what he is saying.

KING ALFRED: So . . . the men are gathering at the forest's

edge . . . already . . . on the very day of the defeat . . . they are only waiting for the sound of the King's horn.

NARRATOR: While he is talking he forgets about the cakes. They are burning. He looks down at the horn. He takes it in his hand.

KING ALFRED: They *will* drive back the Danes.

JOAN: I thought I could smell my cakes burning! Out of my house! Away with you! I will not help a man so stupid. Not if he were the last Englishman left to fight the Danes. Not if he were the King himself. Burned! You blockhead! You numskull! You stupid vagabond!

NARRATOR: The man leaves quickly. A little later as we look in at the woodcutter's simple cottage we find Joan still grumbling about the burned cakes.

JOAN: Now, no cakes to give to Fulke. But only milk. . . . Still, milk in plenty.

FULKE: Joan, oh Joan!

JOAN: Fulke! What news?

FULKE: The men are massing not far off. Each hour more and more men are gathering.

JOAN: But King Alfred? Is there yet news of him?

FULKE: No. No news. No sight nor sound of him. 'Tis feared he could not save himself.

JOAN: When men who're no account go free, why not the King instead? A stupid dolt was here just now, but I sent him on.

FULKE: Ah . . . what was that? The sound of a horn? Yes! The sound of the King's horn!

JOAN: King Alfred's horn!

FULKE: Now England will be saved. But Joan, the vagabond you told me of, whom you sent on but now. What did he look like?

JOAN: Why, ragged he was, with bleeding face, and grime. Yet, now I do recall. Hung from his shoulder was a mighty horn. Oh, Fulke. . . .

FULKE: What was his height? How did he bear himself?

JOAN: Oh, very tall he was. And he used words as we do not. Oh, Fulke.

FULKE: And you sent him on to where the men are gathering.

JOAN: Ay . . . with harsh words. Think you he was the King?

FULKE: Ay, likely so. But do not feel dismay. The King has just one care. Naught else would trouble him.

JOAN: But Fulke, the names I called him. Blockhead I said! And numskull! And stupid vagabond!

FULKE: But he has found his men. You sent him to them! Nothing else matters.

JOAN: And England shall be saved!

FULKE: Ay, England shall be saved!

THE END

Adalmina's Pearl

The family in this play is just like many that you know. The mother and three children are talking together just as you might talk with your own mother. Read the play through quickly to find the answers to these questions:

1. What is Alden's problem?
2. What is wrong with Betty and Barbara?
3. Why did Mother tell the story of Adalmina's Pearl?
4. Do you think the children knew why she told it? What makes you think so?

Now get busy and with the help of your teacher, choose people for the parts in the play. This play is easy to read. No difficult words. No strange ways of putting words together. These people talk just as you do.

Remember:

1. Use your voice to give meaning to the words.
2. Speak clearly and distinctly.
3. Pay attention to punctuation.

Practice reading the play two or three times. When you feel you are ready, tell your teacher and decide on the best time to read it for an audience.

ADALMINA'S PEARL

by Karin Asbrand

Characters

(1 woman, 1 boy, 2 girls, and the narrator)

NARRATOR

MOTHER, *who is something like your own mother. She does not like some of the things she hears her children saying.*

BETTY ⎱ *two nice girls who are very interested in how people*
BARBARA ⎰ *look and dress*

ALDEN, *a bright boy who thinks he knows just about everything*

NARRATOR: Mother is in the sewing room busily working. The children are just arriving home from school. All three, Alden, Betty and Barbara, rush into the room. Alden throws his books down as he speaks.

ALDEN: Hi, Mom. . . . There, old books. In the corner for you. I can't see any sense in going to school all the time and having to work the way I do. I'm smart enough.

BETTY: I suppose you still think you are the smartest one in the room.

ALDEN: In school, you mean? Well, not quite. The teacher is a little smarter than I am, I suppose—in some things.

BARBARA: You certainly think a lot of yourself.

BETTY: Well, and so do you, Barbara. You are always looking in the mirror to see if your hair is just right or something.

BARBARA: I'm really not bad-looking, though, you will have to admit.

MOTHER: Handsome is as handsome does, Barbara.

BARBARA: Whatever that means. Look, there goes that funny-looking Mary Smith. Is she a sight! And what terrible-looking clothes she wears.

BETTY: I'm glad I don't look like her. I wouldn't even speak to her. She's poor, and we're rich.

MOTHER: Sit down here by me, children. I am going to tell you a story.

ALDEN: A fairy story, Mom?

MOTHER: Yes, something like that. It is a story written many years ago by Zacharius Topelius, the Swedish writer, about a little Princess named Adalmina.

BETTY: Was she a real Princess or just make-believe?

MOTHER: She was just make-believe, though she was very real to Topelius.

BARBARA: Was she beautiful?

MOTHER: Oh, yes, very beautiful. When she was christened the King and Queen invited two fairies, the red fairy and the yellow fairy, to be her godparents. The red fairy gave her a large pearl, the most beautiful pearl anyone had ever seen. The fairy told Adalmina's parents that as long as she had that pearl she would become richer, wiser, and more beautiful with each passing day. But if she ever lost the pearl she would lose all three of these gifts, her beauty, her riches, and her wisdom.

ALDEN: Whew, I bet they hung on to that pearl for dear life.

MOTHER: They tried to. The King had the pearl set in a crown of gold that just fit Adalmina's lovely little head. She never went anywhere without that crown. She even wore it to bed.

BARBARA: What did the yellow fairy give her?

MOTHER: She told her that if she ever lost the crown she would receive the gift of a kind heart. So the little Princess grew up. Because the King and Queen were so afraid she would lose the pearl she was never allowed to go any farther than to the big gate between the palace garden and the park. Everywhere she went she had eight servants along with her. Each one was sternly admonished to guard the Princess and the pearl.

BETTY: Tell us more, Mother. Did she lose the pearl?

MOTHER: Just a minute, Betty. Don't rush me, dear. The red fairy was right. Adalmina became the most beautiful Princess in the wide world with riches galore, and so wise was she that philosophers and wise men all over the kingdom marveled at her wisdom.

ALDEN: I bet I could have asked her things she couldn't answer.

MOTHER: Maybe you could, Alden. At any rate, the King and Queen thought that Adalmina was the most perfect being ever created, and, sad to say, Adalmina began to think so, too. She even began to look down on her parents. She became very proud and haughty, and was jealous of anything anybody had that she did not possess. She even trampled down all the beautiful flowers in the garden if anyone happened to admire them. She became a tyrant whom nobody really loved.

BARBARA: And then she lost the pearl!

MOTHER: Goodness, how you rush me. One day, when she was fifteen years old she went walking in the garden with her servants. She wanted to go out into the park, and when they refused to open the gate she climbed the fence and ran away.

ALDEN: I don't know that I blame her much. That was no kind of life, even for a girl.

BARBARA: Where did she go? What happened to her?

MOTHER: She walked until she came to a well. Being thirsty she leaned over to get a drink. She saw her image in the water and admired herself greatly. But, as she was admiring her reflection, her crown fell off into the water—and she lost the pearl. Suddenly her image was changed from that of a lovely Princess into a homely, ragged beggar girl.

BETTY: It served her right.

MOTHER: She was tired and hungry and forlorn. She had forgotten her name and who she had ever been. She walked and walked until she came to a little cottage. The little old lady that lived there took her in, and here is where the yellow fairy's gift came in. Adalmina helped to tend the old lady's goats, and her heart became filled with peace and love for everyone. She learned to love the sunshine and the flowers and all that was good in the world.

ALDEN: And what happened to the King and Queen?

MOTHER: For three years they sought their daughter. Then one day a Prince whose name was Sigismund came along. He stopped by the well. Down in the water he saw something brilliant shining and when he pulled it up there was the crown with the pearl as beautiful as ever. He had stopped by the little cottage and had seen the homely little girl. He had thought how kind and sweet she was.

BARBARA: Did he put the crown on her head?

MOTHER: No, he brought it to the court. The King and Queen ordered all the girls in the kingdom that were eighteen years old to come and try the crown, but it would fit none of them. Finally the Prince said, "There's one more girl who has not tried on this crown. That is the little one who lives with the little old lady. Let us see if it fits her. Certainly it can do no harm." Everybody laughed and scoffed, but the King sent for the girl. The crown was a perfect fit for her, of course, because she was the Princess Adalmina.

BETTY: And did the Prince marry her? Did they live happily ever after?

MOTHER: Yes, of course. Otherwise it would not be a good fairy story. But though the Princess Adalmina got back her beauty, her riches, and her wisdom, her kind heart did not change. Everybody loved her.

BARBARA: I guess poor little Mary Smith can't help it if she is so homely. I'll speak to her tomorrow in school.

BETTY: She can't help it that she is poor because her father is dead, either. Would you let her come here sometime, Mother, and play with us?

MOTHER: Why certainly, I was hoping you would say that. She may come here any time.

ALDEN: Thanks for the story, Mom. When I get a little too wise I guess I'd better remember the story of Adalmina's pearl.

THE END

The Magic Goose is an old fairy tale. You have probably heard it many times before. It takes place at the fair grounds where there are many things to buy and many things to see. When you read the lines, be careful of the rhyming.

You will have to use your voice to express many things.

The King is at first *discouraged* and then *joyful*.
The Princess is *sad* and *weeping* and then *laughing*.
The sisters are *proud, excited, impatient* and *frightened*.
The old man is tired and hungry and *pleading* for food.
The Mayor is very important and full of news.

1. Choose people for the different parts in the play.
2. Read the play through to yourself, paying particular attention to your own part.
3. Practice reading the play together. Help each other with difficult words, with voices, with smooth reading.

If you are King, *be* a King.
If you are Mayor, *be* the Mayor.

Remember to act your part.
Plan a time to read your play to the other children.

THE MAGIC GOOSE

adapted by Deborah Newman

Characters
(4 girls, 12 men, 1 woman, and the narrator)

NARRATOR

SIMON, *a kind boy who came to the fair*

OLD MAN, *a poor man who is very hungry*

1ST SISTER ⎫
2ND SISTER ⎬ *girls who came to the fair to have fun*
3RD SISTER ⎭

BAKER, *a very good cook who is proud of his food, but who is not too kind*

SOLDIER

MAYOR

MAYOR'S WIFE

THE KING, *an unhappy King who would give anything to make his daughter happy*

THE PRINCESS, *a young girl who has never smiled or laughed in all her life*

1ST VENDOR

2ND VENDOR

1ST PEASANT

2ND PEASANT

3RD PEASANT

4TH PEASANT

NARRATOR: Today's play takes us to the fair grounds. Here we see young Simon with a knapsack over his shoulder. He is walking about slowly, looking at the booths. Three sisters are talking with the soldier. The peasants and the vendors are talking. The baker walks up and down holding a tray of cakes and crying his wares. Listen.

BAKER: I've won the baker's prize with cakes and apple pies. My cookies are a great delight to eat. I've sugared tarts in pairs, delicious chocolate squares. Come and buy to give yourself a treat.

OLD MAN: Some food, give me some food, I pray, for I've had not a bite today.

BAKER: If you've no coins, don't bother me. My cakes cannot be eaten free.

OLD MAN: My lassies, dressed up for the fair, have you some coins that you might spare?

1ST SISTER: I do have money, that is true, but *never* for the likes of you.

2ND SISTER: There's finery I've come to buy.

3RD SISTER: I've nothing for you. No, not I!

SOLDIER: Be off, old man! With girls to treat, my coins will go before *I* eat.

OLD MAN: Take pity on my old gray head. Have you, young sir, a piece of bread?

SIMON: I've brought my dinner to the fair and what I have I'll gladly share.

OLD MAN: For kindness I pay handsomely. Dig 'neath the roots of that old tree. A priceless treasure you will find. A prize the dwarf king left behind. Hold it fast beneath your arm till laughter breaks its magic charm.

SIMON: A priceless treasure I must hold? I'll quickly dig. It might be gold!

NARRATOR: Simon goes off to find his treasure. The mayor enters with his wife. The baker goes to them.

BAKER: Your honor, I have apple pie and sugar cakes that you must try.

MAYOR: Oh, listen to the news I bring. You may have baked them for the King!

WIFE: The King is coming, coming here! He hopes to bring his daughter cheer.

MAYOR: Poor Princess. She has never smiled since she was but a tiny child.

BAKER: The King! The Princess! Heavens sakes! I know they'll love my pies and cakes.

1ST SISTER: Oh, is it true, sir? Did you say the Princess would be here today?

SOLDIER: The Princess? I understand the King has offered up her hand. "If someone makes her laugh," he said. "That person shall the Princess wed."

MAYOR: To make her laugh so many tried, and yet the Princess only cried.

2ND SISTER: Why bother with a sour lass who weeps all day, "Alas, alas"?

3RD SISTER: I'm certain that she must be daft. Were I a Princess, *I* would laugh.

WIFE: Oh, hold your tongue, girl. You don't know why our sweet Princess sorrows so.

MAYOR: When she was young, so I've heard tell, the dwarf king cast a magic spell.

NARRATOR: Now here comes Simon. He has something under his arm. Maybe it is the treasure the old man told about. It must be! It is a large golden goose. The sisters see him.

1ST SISTER: Look, sisters . . . look there up ahead. The lad who gave the beggar bread.

2ND SISTER: And oh! Beneath his arm . . . behold! He has a goose of purest gold.

3RD SISTER: He must be royalty in disguise to carry such a precious prize.

1ST SISTER: I'd like to touch your golden goose. Perhaps a feather will pull loose.

2ND SISTER: You think you'll get ahead of me. I'll win him over as you'll see.

1ST SISTER: I'm stuck! The golden goose has glue.

2ND SISTER: I can't pull loose! I'm stuck to you.

3RD SISTER: Enough of all your silly tricks to make me think you're in a fix. *Help!*

SOLDIER: Still, lassies, and rely on me, for I'm the man to set you free.

MAYOR: Young man, you'll be proclaimed a dunce unless this nonsense stops at once. Help! I'm stuck, too. Wife, place your hands around my waist, and pull me free or I'm disgraced.

WIFE: My husband, I shall need help too, for I am now stuck fast to you! Help! Help! Help!

1ST PEASANT: Here! Stop this now! I'll set you free. Help! I, too, am stuck as you can see.

2ND PEASANT: Ridiculous!

3RD PEASANT: We'll set you free.

4TH PEASANT: Why all the fuss? You stupid folk! . . . Help! Help! I, too, am in the yoke!

NARRATOR: Simon leads them around. All are tugging to get free. They are going behind one of the stands. The baker watches them.

BAKER: A lot of sillies in a chain who wanted gold, but all in vain. . . . Why, here are the King and the Princess. How sad she looks. Her eyes are red from crying.

KING: Good friends, we've gone from fair to fair in hopes of finding laughter there. My daughter, we'll stop here a while, for something may cause you to smile.

1ST VENDOR: This puppet's ridiculous nose is so long that it reaches his toes. But he doesn't mind it since *he* is behind it. He follows it wherever it goes.

2ND VENDOR: Dancing, prancing, bright balloons following the wind's gay tunes. Funny faces changing places, tugging harder at their laces. All are fat and round as moons. Won't you have some bright balloons?

KING: When all the world is gay and glad, my daughter, are you still so sad? Come then, my dear, we will be gone. Our search for laughter must go on.

NARRATOR: At this moment Simon, followed by the chain of people, is coming from behind the stand. The people are still struggling and trying to get free. The Princess is smiling! Yes, she is smiling! The people are getting free! They are all falling to the ground! The Princess laughs aloud.

PRINCESS: Tee hee! That was a funny sight! I wondered if my eyes saw right.

KING: Oh, very funny, yes indeed. I'm almost sorry they were freed.

MAYOR: Your Majesty, I'm in disgrace. Such nonsense in a public place.

KING: Such nonsense? No, it was great fun. I wish I knew how it was done.

PRINCESS: To see them pull, to hear them yell! How hard they tugged . . . then down they fell!

KING: Young man, you are a great success. You've brought the Princess happiness.

SIMON: I'm pleased to hear I've done that, sir. I didn't mean to make a stir.

SOLDIER: Remember what you said, my lord. Now you must give him his reward.

KING: Of all my kingdom, you'll get half because you made the Princess laugh.

PRINCESS: And Father, you know what you said. This lad will be the one I'll wed.

MAYOR: Let us have a celebration where I'll make a proclamation to inform our happy nation of this day. Oh, the joy and the elation when I tell the population that we'll have a coronation. Come this way!

THE END

Ali Baba and the Forty Thieves

You all know the story of *Ali Baba and the Forty Thieves* so it should be an easy play for you to read.

Look first at the names of the people and make sure you can pronounce them. Your teacher will help you.

Ali Baba
Morgiana
Cassim
Baba Mustapha

It is most important to watch the punctuation when reading the lines of this play.

Remember: at a comma you make a *short* pause.

at a period you make a longer pause and lower your voice.

at an exclamation point—you cry out, usually with excitement or fear or impatience.

a series of dots . . . means a pause as if you were uncertain, or were thinking, or simply not speaking for a moment because you were doing something.

Try these lines to see how well you can do. Arrange for different children to read the lines:

CASSIM: And what, pray, lies in yonder bags?
ALI BABA: Naught, Brother, naught of any value.
CASSIM: Gold pieces, perhaps?
ALI BABA: Where would I, a poor man, get so many bags full of gold?

Have two or three people try these lines of Cassim's. Be sure to pause at the dots. Be excited at first and then very frightened and finally frantic. Do not read the words in the parentheses. They are to help you to read better.

CASSIM (*Excited*): Gold! . . . Gold! . . . I'll take all I can carry. . . . I'll come back again for more. There is no hurry. . . . (*As though talking to himself*) Now for the magic words to open the door. . . . Open barley! . . . I must have the wrong password! . . . Open pumpkin! . . . No, that's not right, either. (*Frantic. Trying anything. Voice growing louder!*) Open, santo! . . . Open barley! . . . Open pumpkin! Magi open! Open! Open!

Now try these lines of Morgiana's:

MORGIANA (*Puzzled*): A caller? A man, I see, who comes to my master's house but does not enter. What can that mean? . . . Ah, what is this? My master's house is being marked. I shall fool this caller who comes to the door, but does not enter. I shall mark the door of my neighbor's house . . . and of this house . . . and this . . . and this . . . and this. (*Now knowing what to do—voice grows stronger and more certain*) There! Now back to my work.

ALI BABA AND THE FORTY THIEVES

(*an Arabian Nights' Tale*)
adapted by Jerry Felsheim

Characters

(*1 girl, 6 men, and the narrator*)

NARRATOR

ALI BABA, *the man who found the robbers' treasure*

MORGIANA, *Ali Baba's servant*

CASSIM, *Ali Baba's brother*
CHIEF, *the head of the robber band*
1ST ROBBER, *a member of the robber band*
BABA MUSTAPHA, *a shopkeeper*
2ND ROBBER, *a member of the robber band*

NARRATOR: This old Arabian Nights' Tale takes us to the house of Ali Baba. Ali Baba and his brother, Cassim, are talking. Cassim speaks first.

CASSIM: And what, pray, lies in yonder bags?

ALI BABA: Naught, Brother, naught of any value.

CASSIM: Gold pieces, perhaps? These would be of some value, my brother.

ALI BABA: No, no, it's not gold! Where would I, a poor man, get so many bags full of gold?

CASSIM: Brother, that is what I came here to find out. For certainly those bags are filled with gold.

ALI BABA: It is not so, it is not so!

CASSIM: When your slave girl, Morgiana, came to me for the scales, I oiled them well so that whatever you might weigh would cling to them. Here, Brother, is this not a gold piece?

ALI BABA: A gold piece? Why, so it is. I know not of how it came there.

CASSIM: We shall see. I'll turn one bag upside down. . . . Yes, Brother, gold coins. What does a poor man with so much gold? One would think you were brother to the sultan, instead of to Cassim.

ALI BABA: Pray, Brother, I will tell thee all. But breathe not a word to anyone, for then my life would be in great danger.

CASSIM: Yes?

ALI BABA: Early this morning I was walking my mules to their work in the fields. When I came to the heavily-wooded part of the forest, I suddenly heard a clatter of many horses. Being fearful of robbers, I hid behind a shrub. Then such a sight as I beheld! From out of the forest came no less than forty thieves. At their head was one who seemed to be the chief. He stopped at a certain rock and said these strange words, "Open sesame!" Suddenly a wide doorway in the face of the rock opened. The robbers went through the doorway, and, last of all, went their chief. For a long while they stayed within the cave. I still hid behind my shrub, afraid to leave. At last the doorway in the rock flew open again and the chief and his forty thieves came out. The chief said, "Close sesame!" and the doorway closed. Then they all rode away with a great clatter.

CASSIM: Yes? And then?

ALI BABA: Then I said within myself, "While the thieves are away, I, too, will try the magic words and see for myself what lies behind the rock." I said, "Open sesame!" The doorway within the rock opened. I went down many steps built in the rock, until I came to a large cave. In the cave was a strange and wonderful sight—bag upon bag filled with gold. I quickly filled my arms with them and walked up the steps. There I loaded my mules with the gold bags and said, "Close sesame!" whereupon the doorway closed. That is the whole story, Brother. You will keep it a secret?

CASSIM: Yes, Brother, if you but tell me where to find this cave that I, too, may use the magic password and share your good fortune.

ALI BABA: First, Brother, you take the road leading straight to the forest. Then go about twenty paces to the left. . . .

NARRATOR: It is now later that same day. Let us look into the cave of the robbers. Cassim is there.

CASSIM: Gold! . . . Gold! . . . Gold! . . . I'll take all I can carry . . . I'll come back again for more. There is no hurry. . . . Now for the magic words to open the door. . . . Open barley! . . . Open barley! . . . I must have the wrong password! . . . Open pumpkin! . . . Open pumpkin! . . . No, that's not right, either. Open santo! . . . Open barley! . . . Open pumpkin! Santo open! Magi open! Open! Open!

NARRATOR: Cassim beats on the walls. He beats on the door. Wait, there is a light from above. The door is opening.

Cassim rushes up but he is stopped by the Chief and four of his thieves!

CHIEF: How came you here?

1ST ROBBER: He has discovered our secret. We must kill him!

CHIEF: Not before he tells us all. How came you here?

CASSIM: O please, O master, I did but fall in here, I know not how.

CHIEF: It is not true. Take him and kill him.

CASSIM: No, no, no! I will tell you. I will tell you everything. My brother, Ali Baba, was here this morn, hiding behind a shrub. He saw everything. After you had left he used the magic password and came down here and took away much gold. Then he told me about it and bade me take some, too. But when I would leave, I had forgotten the password.

CHIEF: One of us must go at once to the town and find out where this Ali Baba lives. We must fetch him here before he tells all Mecca about our gold and our magic password. Go, you, to the town and put a cross on the house which is Ali Baba's. Then come back to me, and together we will go into Mecca and avenge ourselves. Before we are through, we shall kill Ali Baba, too.

1ST ROBBER: Yes, O Chief! At once. Open sesame!

NARRATOR: Let's follow the First Robber. We find him in the shop of Baba Mustapha. Listen!

1ST ROBBER: Pray tell me, good fellow, where is the house of Ali Baba?

BABA MUSTAPHA: There goes Morgiana, the slave of Ali Baba. Follow her with your eyes and you will soon see the house for which you are asking.

1ST ROBBER: A thousand thanks, my good fellow.

NARRATOR: The Robber waits until he sees Morgiana enter Ali Baba's house. Now he is following. He is putting a chalk mark on the front door! Morgiana has been watching, though. As soon as the Robber is out of sight, she comes out.

MORGIANA: A caller? A man, I see, who comes to my master's

house but does not enter. What can that mean? . . . Ah, what is this? My master's house is being marked. I shall fool this caller who comes to the door, but does not enter. I shall mark the door of our neighbor's house . . . and of this house . . . and this . . . and this . . . and this. There! Now, back to my work.

1ST ROBBER: O Chief! Straight to the house I shall take you. Here is the house. See, O Chief, the mark I have made with my chalk!

CHIEF: But all the houses are marked with chalk. Which house do you mean?

1ST ROBBER: O Chief, this is not the work of my hand! Only Ali Baba's house did I mark.

CHIEF: If you are so wise, then tell me which house did you mark! Which is the house of Ali Baba, who stole our gold?

1ST ROBBER: O kind Chief, merciful Chief, forgive me! Forgive me! That I no longer can tell.

CHIEF: Fool! You great fool! I shall find out in this shop. . . .

1ST ROBBER: O kind Chief, have you learned the house?

CHIEF: Yes. Away from me, you fool! And stand with the lowest! Tonight I shall come back disguised as an oil merchant. I shall call at the house of Ali Baba and ask for lodging for the night. I shall have many oil barrels with me, for I am a great merchant. These barrels will stand on all sides of Ali Baba's house. In each barrel one of you will be hidden. You will stay there until I give the signal. The signal will be two short whistles. When you hear them, you will jump out of the barrels and come running into the house. Then we shall slay Ali Baba, the man who stole our gold. So we shall avenge ourselves. Is this clear?

NARRATOR: It is now evening, shortly before dinnertime. All around Ali Baba's house stand oil barrels. Morgiana speaks to her master. Listen.

MORGIANA: Master, dinner will be ready soon. Shall I set a place for Cassim?

ALI BABA: Cassim has not yet returned.

MORGIANA: O master, I fear Cassim will never return. I fear the robbers have captured him.

ALI BABA: Why do you think that?

MORGIANA: Strange men have come to your house and put strange marks on your door. I fear Cassim has told the robbers who you are and where you live. Your life may be in danger.

ALI BABA: You speak foolishly, girl. Go back into the house and see that everything is ready for dinner. An oil merchant, from a distant country, asked for lodging in my house for the night. He will be dining with us tonight. See all the barrels of oil he has brought with him. Forty of them!

MORGIANA: An oil merchant? Good, that is just what we want. Throughout the house we are in need of oil. I will look to see if one of the barrels is open.

NARRATOR: Morgiana goes out and walks toward one of the barrels. She is about to lift the cover, but instead she listens . . . and hears a loud whisper.

1ST ROBBER: O Chief, this barrel is small, and I am getting cramped. Will you give us the signal soon?

NARRATOR: Morgiana jumps back in surprise. She is leaving the first barrel and is running to the second. Again there is a loud whisper. . . .

2ND ROBBER: O Chief, when are you going to whistle and allow us to jump out of this cramped place? It is so uncomfortable here that it makes me want to cut Ali Baba into a thousand pieces.

NARRATOR: Morgiana is now back in the house. The Chief, dressed as a merchant, and Ali Baba are sitting on cushions on the floor waiting for dinner. Morgiana comes into the room. She is carrying a steaming pitcher of oil. Ali Baba speaks to her.

ALI BABA: Morgiana, dinner may be served.

MORGIANA: Yes, O master.

ALI BABA: Did you not hear me? We await the evening meal.

MORGIANA: Yes, O master, but I needed oil, and so went to

our neighbor's house to borrow it. Now I am returning what was not used.

ALI BABA: Why did you not ask my guest, the oil merchant, if you might use some of his? There are many oil barrels near the house.

CHIEF: Yes, yes.

MORGIANA: I am sorry, master. I did not know if I should. As soon as this boiling oil is returned, I shall serve dinner.

ALI BABA: Morgiana! Morgiana! Come here at once!

CHIEF: A strange slave girl. Does she not obey her master?

ALI BABA: Always, O merchant. But we have been troubled of late. My brother, Cassim by name, went forth on an errand early this morning and has not yet returned.

CHIEF: Surely that can be no cause for alarm. His mules may have been slow or he may have tarried by the wayside.

ALI BABA: That is not like Cassim. He is not one who tarries by the wayside. No, I am fearful that some ill has befallen him. Morgiana is fearful, too. That is why she seems to disobey.

MORGIANA: O master, I have returned the boiling oil. Now dinner shall be served.

CHIEF: Ali Baba, you may think I jest, but I have a wish I should like to make.

ALI BABA: I shall not think your wish a jest. Say what you have in mind. If it is within my power, merchant, the wish shall be yours.

CHIEF: Before we eat, in my country, we drive away the evil spirits. We do this by giving two sharp whistles . . . thus.

ALI BABA: Two sharp whistles? But why?

CHIEF: To warn evil spirits that they are being watched. . . . Why don't they come?

MORGIANA: O master, I think the evil spirits are asleep.

CHIEF: Why do you think so? What reason have you for thinking so?

MORGIANA: O merchant, have you not said so yourself? That with two whistles you drive away evil spirits?

CHIEF: You have a quick tongue in your head. Where did you take that steaming oil? Where?

MORGIANA: To the neighbor I borrowed it from.

CHIEF: Did you not pour that oil into my barrels? Did you not?

MORGIANA: Yes. They are oil barrels, are they not? What better place for oil than oil barrels?

ALI BABA: Morgiana, mind your place!

CHIEF: And you poured the burning oil into all forty of my barrels?

MORGIANA: Yes.

CHIEF: Allah! Allah! Allah!

NARRATOR: The Chief is clutching something under his cloak. It is a dagger! He is about to grab Morgiana! She is too quick for him, though. She is picking up a long knife from the table. She's stabbed him! He is dead. Ali Baba jumps up.

ALI BABA: What have you done? You have killed an honorable merchant! A guest! A stranger! Wicked girl!

MORGIANA: Master, pray, I did what was best for you. This is no honorable merchant. He is the Chief of the Forty Thieves. When I went out to fetch the oil for the house, I heard strange voices coming from the barrels. "When shall you give the signal, O Chief?" said the voice from the first barrel. "It is so uncomfortable here that it makes me want to cut Ali Baba into a thousand pieces" came from the second barrel. There was a thief in each of the forty barrels. So I hurried to our neighbor's house and borrowed some oil which I boiled. Then I poured oil on them until they were dead. When the Chief, disguised as this merchant, whistled, no one came. Then he was angry and would have killed us both.

ALI BABA: So it was your hand which struck first! Morgiana, you are a good girl. You have saved my life! I give you your freedom.

THE END

A Mad Tea Party

A Mad Tea Party is taken from the story of *Alice in Wonderland*. Alice has gone down the rabbit hole and is in a
strange upside-down world of peculiar people.

The fun in this play is its nonsense. The conversation jumps
and hops about without "rhyme or reason". There is a great
deal of playing with the different meanings of words and twisting them about.

Here is a good example of twisting words around. Choose
a boy and girl to try these lines. Read slowly to be sure the
listener can get every word:

HATTER: Why is a raven like a writing desk?

ALICE: I believe I can guess that.

MARCH HARE: Do you mean you think you know the
answer to it?

ALICE: Exactly.

MARCH HARE: Then you should say what you mean.

ALICE: I do . . . at least I mean what I say. . . . That's
the same thing, you know.

HATTER: Not the same thing at all! Why, you might just
as well say "I see what I eat" is the same as "I eat what
I see".

MARCH HARE: You might just as well say that "I like what
I get" is the same thing as "I get what I like."

DORMOUSE: You might just as well say that "I breathe
when I sleep" is the same thing as "I sleep when I
breathe."

Think about how silly they have made Alice's remark seem.
The whole play is like this and will be amusing to the listener

only if in reading you are sure that these lines can be understood.

Decide who is going to play the different characters.

Practice reading the play together. Check each other on
these points:

> Are your voices clear?
>
> Are you changing your voices to show surprise, anger,
> impatience, uncertainty?
>
> Are you coming in with your parts promptly?

When you are sure you have done a good job, check with
your teacher and arrange to read for the other children.

A MAD TEA PARTY

adapted from Alice in Wonderland
by Natalie S. Worcester

Characters

(1 girl, 3 boys, and the narrator)

NARRATOR

ALICE, *a little girl with long golden hair who finds herself in a*
strange land

THE MARCH HARE ⎫ *three characters who are having a very*
THE DORMOUSE   ⎬ *strange tea party*
THE HATTER   ⎭

NARRATOR: No doubt you have read the story of *Alice in*
Wonderland or maybe you have seen it in the movies. Do
you remember the Mad Tea Party with the March Hare,
the Mad Hatter, and the Dormouse? Alice is just arriving
at the party. The March Hare speaks to her. Listen.

MARCH HARE: No room!

HATTER: There's no room!

ALICE: There's *plenty* of room.

MARCH HARE: Have some wine.

ALICE: I don't see any wine.

MARCH HARE: There isn't any.

ALICE: Then it wasn't very nice of you to offer it.

MARCH HARE: It wasn't very nice of you to sit down without being invited.

ALICE: I didn't know it was *your* table.

HATTER: Your hair needs cutting.

ALICE: You should learn not to make personal remarks. It's very rude.

HATTER: Why is a raven like a writing desk?

ALICE: I believe I can guess that.

MARCH HARE: Do you mean you think you know the answer to it?

ALICE: Exactly.

MARCH HARE: Then you should say what you mean.

ALICE: I do . . . at least . . . at least I mean what I say. . . . That's the same thing, you know.

HATTER: Not the same thing at all! Why, you might just as well say "I see what I eat" is the same thing as "I eat what I see".

MARCH HARE: You might just as well say that "I like what I get" is the same thing as "I get what I like".

DORMOUSE: You might as well say that "I breathe when I sleep" is the same thing as "I sleep when I breathe".

HATTER: It *is* the same thing with you. . . . My watch isn't going. . . . What day of the month is it?

ALICE: The fourth.

HATTER: Two days wrong. I told you butter wouldn't suit the works.

MARCH HARE: It was the *best* butter.

HATTER: Yes, but some crumbs must have got in as well. You shouldn't have put it in with the bread knife.

MARCH HARE: It was the *best* butter, you know.

ALICE: What a funny watch! It tells the day of the month and doesn't tell what o'clock it is!

HATTER: Why should it? Does *your* watch tell you what year it is?

ALICE: Of course not! But that's because it stays the same year for such a long time.

HATTER: Which is just the case with *mine*.

ALICE: I don't quite understand you.

HATTER: The Dormouse is asleep again. I'll pour a little tea on his nose.

DORMOUSE: Of course, of course. Just what I was going to remark myself.

HATTER: Have you guessed the riddle yet?

ALICE: No. I give up. What's the answer?

HATTER: I haven't the slightest idea.

MARCH HARE: Nor I.

ALICE: I think you might do something better with the time than wasting it asking riddles that have no answers.

HATTER: If you knew Time as well as I do you wouldn't talk about wasting *it*. It's *him*.

ALICE: I don't know what you mean.

HATTER: Of course you don't. I dare say you never even spoke to Time.

ALICE: Perhaps not, but I know I have to *beat* time when I learn music.

HATTER: Ah, that accounts for it. He won't stand beating. Now if you only kept on good terms with him, he'd do almost anything you liked with the clock. For instance, suppose it were nine o'clock in the morning . . . just in time to begin lessons. You'd only have to whisper a hint to Time and round goes the clock in a twinkling. Half-past one, time for dinner.

MARCH HARE: I only wish it were.

ALICE: That would be nice. But then I shouldn't be hungry for it, you know.

HATTER: Not at first perhaps, but you could keep it to half-past one for as long as you liked.

ALICE: Is that the way you manage?

HATTER: Not I. We quarreled last March, just before *he* went mad, you know. The March Hare, I mean. It was at the great concert given by the Queen of Hearts and I had to sing:

"Twinkle, twinkle, little bat
How I wonder what you're at. . . ."

You know the song perhaps?

ALICE: I've heard something like it.

HATTER: It goes on, you know, in this way:

"Up above the world you fly
Like a tea tray in the sky.
Twinkle, twinkle. . . ."

DORMOUSE: Twinkle, twinkle, twinkle, twinkle. . . .

HATTER: Pinch him. Pinch that Dormouse. . . . As I was saying, I'd hardly finished the first verse when the Queen bawled, "Off with his head!"

ALICE: How dreadfully savage!

HATTER: And ever since that, Time won't do a thing I ask. It's always six o'clock now.

ALICE: Is that the reason so many tea things are put out here?

HATTER: Yes, that's it. It's always tea time and we've no time to wash the things in between.

ALICE: Then you keep moving around, I suppose.

HATTER: Exactly, as the things get used up.

ALICE: But what happens when you come to the beginning again?

MARCH HARE: Suppose we change the subject. I'm getting tired of this. I vote the young lady tell us a story.

ALICE: I'm afraid I don't know one.

MARCH HARE: Then the Dormouse shall. Wake up, Dormouse.

DORMOUSE: I wasn't asleep. I heard every word you fellows were saying.

MARCH HARE: Tell us a story!

ALICE: Yes, please do!

HATTER: And be quick about it or you'll be asleep again before you're through.

DORMOUSE: Once upon a time there were three little sisters. Their names were Elsie, Lacie, and Tillie and they lived at the bottom of a well. . . .

ALICE: What did they live on?

DORMOUSE: They lived on treacle.

ALICE: They couldn't have done that, you know. They would have been ill.

DORMOUSE: So they were. *Very* ill.

ALICE: But why did they live at the bottom of a well?

MARCH HARE: Take some more tea.

ALICE: I've had nothing yet so I can't take more.

HATTER: You mean you can't take *less*. It's very easy to take more than nothing.

ALICE: Nobody asked *your* opinion.

HATTER: Who's making personal remarks now?

ALICE: Why did they live at the bottom of the well?

DORMOUSE: It was a treacle well.

ALICE: There's no such thing!

HATTER: Shhhhhhhh!

DORMOUSE: If you can't be civil, you'd better finish the story yourself.

ALICE: No, please go on. I won't interrupt you again. I daresay there may be *one*.

DORMOUSE: *One* indeed! And so these three little sisters—they were learning to draw, you know.

ALICE: What did they draw?

DORMOUSE: Treacle.

HATTER: I want a clean cup. Let's all move over one place.

ALICE: But I don't understand. Where did they draw the treacle from?

HATTER: You can draw water out of a water well so I should think you could draw treacle out of a treacle well, eh, stupid?

ALICE: But they were *in* the well.

DORMOUSE: Of course they were. *Well in.* . . . They were learning to draw and they drew all manner of things . . . everything that begins with an M.

ALICE: Why an M?

MARCH HARE: Why not?

DORMOUSE: . . . That begins with an M such as mousetraps . . . and the moon and memory and muchness . . . you know you say things are much of a muchness?

ALICE: Really, now that you ask, I don't think. . . .

HATTER: Then you shouldn't talk.

ALICE: I'm leaving . . . I'll never go *there* again. It's the stupidest tea party I ever was at in all my life!

THE END

SECTION TWO

Voice Directions

In reading a play it is often necessary to use your voice in such a way that you sound angry, frightened, or impatient. If this is not done, the play may become uninteresting and lacking in meaning.

Because the author, too, feels this is very important to play reading, he often inserts a word to tell you how to use your voice. In the plays you have just completed, these words, called "voice directions," were omitted.

Look at the samples below:

MOTHER (*Worried*): Oh! I do wish John would come home. I am so worried.

or

BETTY (*Crying*): Please help me. I am so frightened.

or

FATHER (*Quickly*): Look out, Bob! A car is coming!

The words in the parentheses tell you how to use your voice. They should help you to read better. *Do not read them aloud.*

Practice some of these lines with your teacher. Follow the *voice directions*. Did you sound worried? Did you cry? Did you speak quickly? Try again if you think it will help.

Hansel and Gretel

You all know the fairy story of *Hansel and Gretel*. This is the same story made into a play. Read it to yourselves.

Think for a few minutes about the characters in the story.

What kind of man is the woodcutter?

How would you describe him?

How do you think he felt?

How do you think his wife felt?

Which of these words describe them: happy, tired, discouraged, frightened, young, cruel, unhappy?

Which words describe the voices they would use: quick, bright, light, laughing, slow, heavy, discouraged, tired, unhappy?

How would you describe the witch?

Which of these words would you choose to tell about her: sly, kind, cruel, sweet, happy, mean, young, beautiful, ugly, old, sneaky?

Which of the following words might be used to describe the witch's voice: cracked, shrill, soft, sweet, laughing, nasal, low, high?

Hansel and Gretel are just like any other children left alone in the woods. They are tired, hungry, and frightened. They try to think of what to do. They are happy and sad, frightened and glad depending on what takes place in the story.

Now have someone try some of the Witch's lines.

What kind of voice will you use?

"What lovely children! Were you eating my house?"
"In you go! And there you stay until we fatten you up!"
"I've waited long enough. Girl! Climb in the oven and see if it's hot."

Did you like the way the lines were read?

Did she sound old? cruel? sneaky? angry? impatient?

Let someone else try.

Now let some boy and girl try to be the woodcutter and his wife.

> WOODCUTTER: No luck. What are we to do? No one will buy my wood. How can we feed ourselves and the children?
>
> WIFE: I have a plan. It sounds cruel but it's the only way. Tomorrow when you go to the woods, we must take the children and leave them there. Someone will find them there. They will take better care of them than we can.
>
> WOODCUTTER: I wish there were some other way.
>
> WIFE: If we keep them here, we will all starve. Surely it's kinder to give them a chance.

Did these people come in on time?

Did they sound as if they were talking together?

Did you feel that they were tired and discouraged?

How could they have improved their reading?

Let two other children try.

Now choose people for the different characters.

1. Read your parts to yourselves.

2. Practice reading together. Go somewhere so that others cannot hear you. Note the voice directions.

3. When you are ready, plan with the teacher the best time for reading the play to the class.

You should not have trouble with any of the words. If you do, ask for help from the other children or from the teacher.

HANSEL AND GRETEL

adapted by Natalie Simonds

Characters

(1 boy, 1 girl, 1 man, 2 women, and the narrator)

NARRATOR

WOODCUTTER ⎫ *parents of Hansel and Gretel. They are very*
HIS WIFE   ⎭ *poor and very worried*

HANSEL ⎫
GRETEL ⎭ *a small boy and girl who are left alone in the woods*

THE WITCH, *an ugly, cruel, old woman*

NARRATOR: Today we bring you the story of "Hansel and Gretel". As our play opens, the poor Woodcutter has just come home from the market with his load of wood. He puts the wood on the floor near the fireplace and sinks into the nearest chair. His wife looks up and speaks.

WIFE: What luck today?

WOODCUTTER: No luck. What are we to do? No one will buy my wood. How can we feed ourselves and the children?

WIFE (*Hesitantly*): I have a plan. It sounds cruel, but it's the only way. Tomorrow when you go to the woods, we must take the children and leave them there. We can give them food and build a fire to keep them warm. Someone will find them there. They will take better care of them than we can.

WOODCUTTER: I wish there were some other way.

WIFE: If we keep them here, we will all starve. We've scarcely enough food for tomorrow. Surely it's kinder to give them that chance than to let them starve slowly.

WOODCUTTER (*Sighing*): Perhaps you're right. Then come, let us go to bed. We must be up with the sun.

NARRATOR: The next morning very early, the whole family

went to the woods. Now it is late in the afternoon and we find Hansel and Gretel alone in the woods.

GRETEL (*Weeping*): Oh, Hansel, I'm so tired. We've walked and walked and I just can't go any further. Can't we sit down and rest?

HANSEL: Please don't cry, Gretel. I know you're tired, but soon we'll find some nice people who will take us in and give us food and a warm place to sleep.

GRETEL: But why can't we go home, Hans? You said you would scatter our bread so that we could find our way back. We threw away a whole piece of bread and now I'm hungry and the bread is gone.

HANSEL (*Softly*): I know. But the birds ate the bread. (*Cheerfully*) Perhaps they are hungrier than we are. Gretel! Look! A house! Such a pretty little house! Gretel! Come here! The house is made of candy! Real candy!

GRETEL: Oh, Hansel, it's wonderful. A candy house—and all for us!

HANSEL: Somebody's coming! An old woman!

WITCH: What lovely children! Were you eating my house?

HANSEL: Y-y-yes, we were. I hope you won't mind. But it's such a lovely tasting house and we're awfully hungry.

WITCH: You poor children! You must come in and warm yourselves and I'll give you something to eat. I've a place where you can sleep, too.

HANSEL: Oh, thank you. We'd like that.

WITCH: Come ahead.

NARRATOR: In the morning we find Hansel and Gretel asleep on cots in the house of the old Witch.

WITCH: What nice children! They'll make a tasty morsel. I should get three good meals out of them. The boy *is* a bit thin, but I can fatten him up. I'll eat the girl first. She looks about ready now.

HANSEL: Did I sleep long? It's morning, isn't it? I guess I was awfully tired.

WITCH: You were sleeping so soundly I didn't want to wake you. Would you like some breakfast?

HANSEL: Oh, yes! If it isn't too much trouble.

WITCH: Of course not, you dear boy. Come with me to the cupboard and we'll see what we can find. . . . Now . . . what do you see?

HANSEL: Why, it's so dark, I can't. . . .

WITCH: *In you go!* And there you stay until we fatten you up!

HANSEL: Let me out! Let me out!

WITCH (*Chuckling*): Not yet, my boy, not yet. But soon . . . when you're nice and fat. . . . Wake up, girl! Wake up, I say. You've work to do.

GRETEL (*Sleepily*): What's the matter . . . ? Where's my brother?

WITCH: Your brother is in the cupboard with the rest of the food. You're to get busy and cook so that we can fatten him up. Then we'll see about cooking you. Now get about your business.

NARRATOR: A few days later as Gretel is busy working at the stove we hear the Witch speaking to her.

WITCH: We'll see how your brother is getting on. He must be about ready for eating. I'm tired of waiting. If he isn't fat now, I'll eat him anyway. . . . Boy, put your finger out and let me see if you're fattening up. . . . Still pretty bony. I can't see very well, but it doesn't *feel* much fatter. I've waited long enough. I'm going to eat the boy today. Girl! Climb in the oven and see if it's hot.

GRETEL: I don't know how.

WITCH (*Impatiently*): Stupid! I'll show you.

NARRATOR: The Witch goes to the oven and pokes her head in. Gretel jumps behind her and gives her a push. The Witch falls into the oven and Gretel slams the door shut. Then she runs to the cupboard, unlocks it, and lets Hansel out!

HANSEL: What have you done with the Witch?

GRETEL (*Laughing*): I'm cooking her. But let's not stay for dinner. We'll start for home and take something to eat on the way.

HANSEL: I know where she hides her gold! I watched her through the hole in the cupboard while she was counting it. . . . Here it is! See, Gretel! Bags and bags of gold! And look! Jewels! If we can find our way home with this, we'll be rich and Father won't have to leave us in the forest again.

GRETEL: Oh, Hansel, if we only *could* find our way home.

HANSEL: Don't you worry. We will. Now, fetch me that cloak from the corner and we'll wrap the gold and jewels in it.

NARRATOR: Back in the Woodcutter's cottage, the Woodcutter is sitting in a chair. He is very lonely and sad. Hansel and Gretel enter. Gretel goes to her father and touches him gently.

GRETEL: Father, it's Gretel.

WOODCUTTER: Gretel! No, it can't be. . . . How could I have been so wicked?

HANSEL: But we *are* here, Father. We're safe.

WOODCUTTER: My children! You're safe! Thank Heaven! Thank Heaven! I'll never let you go again. No matter what happens. Oh, my children, can you ever forgive me?

GRETEL: Of course, Father. Everything is all right now.

HANSEL: And Father, we're rich!

WOODCUTTER: Rich? What do you mean?

HANSEL: Wait. . . . I'll show you what we've brought.

WOODCUTTER (*Astonished*): Gold! Jewels! I cannot believe my eyes. But even without these, I would still be a rich man, my children, because you are home with me again.

THE END

Return of the Nina

Each person taking part in the play must be very wide awake and ready to read his part at exactly the right time. Long pauses until people get ready spoil the play for those who are listening.

Practice using your voices to show different feelings.

Allow several different people to read each line and decide who did it best and why.

Exercise 1.

Read this line as if you were a mother or father who was very cross:

"Stop making that noise this instant!"

Read this line as if you were fearful of waking someone, not cross, yet you mean what you say:

"Don't make a noise or you'll wake the baby."

Read this line as if you were just coming out of your house and saw a friend you'd like to play with:

"Hi, Bob! Come on over and we'll play ball."

Answer the above line as if you felt uninterested:

"No, you go ahead. I don't want to play."

Exercise 2.

Choose two people to read the following lines.

Remember: 1. You must use your voice to give the meaning.
2. You must come in with your part on time.

BEATRIZ: I think it's silly to waste time when we could be having fun.

JUAN: I am waiting for the return of my father's ship.

BEATRIZ (*Impatiently*): Oh, the fishing fleet won't be in until sunset.

JUAN: My father isn't fishing. He left Palos last August.

BEATRIZ (*Surprised*): Last August? So long ago? It's almost a year.

JUAN: Thirty-two weeks.

BEATRIZ: It is impossible!

Now let us prepare to read the play.

First: With your chairman's help choose a person for each part. Read what it says at the beginning of the play about each character.

Second: Read the play to yourself. Ask for help on any words you do not know. Watch your periods, commas, question marks, and voice directions.

Third: Read your own part two or three times.

Fourth: Now find some place where you can practice reading aloud together. Help each other to come in on time.

Be sure the play sounds smooth and makes sense.

When you are ready, tell the teacher and plan for time to read it to the class.

This may help you to say the names correctly:

    Beatriz—Bee′-ah-triz

    Juan—Wahn

    Alfredo—Al-fray′-dō

    Pablo—Pahb′-lō

    Carlos—Carl′-ōs

    Maria—Mah-rē′-ah

    Isobel—Is′-ō-bel

    Jose—Hō-say′

    Nina—Nee′-nah

    Palos—Pay′-lōs

    Tio Felipe—Tee′-o Fay-lee′-pay

RETURN OF THE NINA

by Esther MacLellan and Catherine V. Schroll

Characters

(1 boy, 1 girl, 3 women, 6 men, and the narrator)

BEATRIZ, *a friend of Juan's*

JUAN, *a young boy whose father sailed across the ocean with Columbus. He is proud of his father and wants to be a sailor, too.*

JUAN'S MOTHER, *worried because her husband has been gone so long. She has no money and does not know what to do.*

TIO FELIPE, *an older man who has plenty of money. He is trying to get Juan to leave the sea and work on his farm.*

ALFREDO
PABLO
CARLOS   *people gathered together to talk about Columbus*
MARIA   *and his men*
ISOBEL
JOSE

COLUMBUS, *tired, but thankful and happy to be safe at home*

NARRATOR: As you know, Columbus discovered America on October 12, 1492. Does anyone know when he returned to Palos in Spain after he made this discovery? Listen to Juan and his friend, Beatriz. They are sitting on a log near the harbor of Palos looking out to sea.

BEATRIZ: I think it's silly to waste time when we could be having fun.

JUAN: I am waiting for the return of my father's ship.

BEATRIZ (*Impatiently*): Oh, the fishing fleet won't be in till sunset.

JUAN: My father isn't fishing. He sailed on the *Nina*, and the *Nina* left Palos last August. August 3, 1492.

BEATRIZ (*Surprised*): Last August? So long ago? It's almost a year.

JUAN: Thirty-two weeks. I have marked the time.

BEATRIZ: No sailor has ever been at sea for thirty-two weeks. It is impossible.

JUAN: No sailor before has ever traveled west to the Indies, Beatriz.

BEATRIZ: To the Indies? Then your father went with Columbus?

JUAN: Yes.

BEATRIZ: I have heard my father and my uncles speak of him. They say Columbus and his ships are surely lost. They say no one can cross the great ocean.

JUAN: *They* say. What do *they* know? Everything has to be done for the first time.

BEATRIZ (*Slowly*): I suppose so. But I'd be scared. I'd rather wait until someone tried it first.

JUAN: That's the way with most people. My father is different. He is brave. And he wanted to go with Columbus for one brave man knows another, you see.

MOTHER: Ah, here you are, my son. Always in the same place, looking out over the broad Atlantic.

JUAN: Yes, Mother.

MOTHER: It is useless, my boy, useless. We must face the truth. Your father is lost.

JUAN: No, Mother, no. That is not the truth.

MOTHER: The *Nina* has been gone for thirty-two weeks, since the third of last August. I know how many days have passed. I have counted them with my tears.

JUAN: It is long, Mother, but the Indies are far away.

BEATRIZ: No one knows how many weeks of sailing are needed to reach the Indies, for no one has ever tried it. Juan explained it to me.

JUAN: That's it, Mother. Don't you understand? Sailing west to reach the East is new. It isn't the same as taking a ship to . . . to Portugal.

MOTHER (*Sighing*): I hope that you are right. But if your father is gone much longer, how are we to live? I have scarcely a penny left.

JUAN: Can't Tio Felipe lend us some? He is rich.

MOTHER: Tio Felipe says that he didn't get rich by lending money to his poor relations.

JUAN: But just a little? Surely he cannot be so cruel as to let us starve?

MOTHER: Your Tio Felipe is not cruel. He has offered to loan me money if. . . . Ah, Felipe! How are you?

TIO FELIPE: I knew I'd find you here. Juan, you are a lazy scamp.

MOTHER: No, no, Tio Felipe. Juan is a good boy. He works hard to help me.

TIO FELIPE: Then why does he waste so much time at the harbor?

MOTHER: The boy looks for the *Nina*, his father's ship.

TIO FELIPE: Such nonsense! Columbus and his men are lost. Lost months ago. A crazy scheme! Sailing west across the Atlantic! Who ever heard of such a thing?

JUAN: Why crazy, Tio Felipe? The world is round. All the wise men say so.

TIO FELIPE: *Say* so, yes. It's easy enough to *say* so. The doing is quite another matter. Perhaps the world is round. I agree to that.

MOTHER: Then sailing west to reach the east is sensible.

TIO FELIPE: Not to a sailor. Not to a sailor! When younger I went to sea. I know what I'm talking about. No ship could withstand the wild gales that sweep across the Atlantic. *No* ship. Besides, who knows how wide the ocean really is?

JUAN: Columbus says that it is narrow.

TIO FELIPE: *Says.* There's that "says" again. But who *knows?* Enough of this idle talk. Have you told the boy?

MOTHER: No, not yet.

TIO FELIPE: Then do so now.

MOTHER: Your uncle says he will help us, Juan, if only. . . .

RETURN OF THE NINA 73

JUAN: Yes?

MOTHER: If only you consent to leave Palos and work on his farm.

JUAN: But, Mother! Tio Felipe's farm is miles and miles from the ocean. How can I leave the sea? You know I am going to be a sailor like Father. If I go to the farm, I'll be there all my life! I'll never get on a ship!

MOTHER: I know, dear. But what are we to do?

BEATRIZ: Don't go, Juan.

JUAN: Farming is fine for some, Tio Felipe, but not for the men of Palos. I'd rather starve than leave the ocean.

TIO FELIPE: Brave words, boy, brave words. I hope you can eat them. Not a penny of mine will go to a nephew who won't work.

JUAN: I'll work. I'll fish and scrub decks and. . . .

ALFREDO: There it is! There it is! There's the ship!

PABLO: It cannot be. You are mistaken, Alfredo.

ALFREDO: I, mistaken! No, indeed.

CARLOS: Alfredo is right. I sailed on her myself, and a fine little vessel she was.

MARIA: Is it true? Has my son at last reached home?

ISOBEL: After all these weary weeks and months of waiting! It's a miracle, that's what it is, a miracle!

TIO FELIPE: What's all this fuss? What's all this nonsense?

BEATRIZ: It's a ship. See her rounding the curve in the river?

JUAN: I do! I do! Oh, Mother! It's the *Nina!*

MOTHER: Are you sure, my boy?

JUAN: How could I be wrong? I would know Father's ship on a dark night in a fog. It's the *Nina*, all right.

MOTHER: Father is home at last! My son, how thankful we must be.

JUAN: Home from the Indies! What stories he will tell!

CARLOS: The brave Columbus was right after all.

ALFREDO: How I wish now that I had gone. All the crew will be rich!

JOSE: I would have sailed had I been a few years younger.

Adventure! Riches! With a leader like Columbus the plan was sure to come right.

PABLO: But the *Nina*, traveling alone? Where is the flagship, the *Santa Maria*?

ALFREDO: Perhaps Columbus didn't reach the Indies after all. Perhaps the *Santa Maria* went down with all hands lost. Perhaps only the *Nina* turned back in time to be saved.

JOSE: Perhaps! Perhaps! I don't believe it.

CARLOS: Nor I. The *Nina* is a better ship, that's the truth of the matter. The *Santa Maria* will be limping along in a day or two.

JUAN: Columbus would never give up! He's reached the Indies.

MOTHER: I pray that you are right.

ALFREDO: We will find out in a moment. The *Nina* has anchored and sent off a boat. Who is that in front? Is it Columbus?

JOSE: That's Columbus. No doubt about it.

ISOBEL: Who are those men with him, dressed so strangely?

PABLO: How queerly they are colored!

MARIA: Who ever saw the like? They have red skins.

JUAN: It is Columbus returned at last. What do you say now, Tio Felipe? It was possible to sail west across the Atlantic, if men were brave enough to try.

TIO FELIPE: What do I say, boy? I say I was wrong. And for once I'm glad to be wrong. This day, March . . . what day is it?

JUAN: March 15, 1493.

TIO FELIPE: This day, March 15, 1493, is a great day for Spain a day that will live forever.

MARIA: And a great day for all wives and mothers of the men on board.

BEATRIZ: Don't forget Columbus! It is a great day for Columbus, too.

COLUMBUS: Did I hear you say a great day for Columbus? Indeed it is.

CARLOS: Welcome home, sir. Welcome to Palos.

PABLO: Tell us, Admiral, what of the Indies?

ALFREDO: Are they as rich as people say?

JOSE: Did you find gold?

ISOBEL: My husband, is he alive?

CARLOS: What of the *Santa Maria*? Is she lost?

COLUMBUS: Friends! The *Santa Maria* is gone. . . .

MARIA: My son! He sailed on the *Santa Maria!* He is lost!

COLUMBUS: No, no, all lives were spared. The men are safe.

MOTHER: The men are safe. What beautiful words!

COLUMBUS: As for the rest, let questions wait till later. We go now to the Cathedral to offer thanks for our safe return.

TIO FELIPE: Come niece, come Juan, and Beatriz, too. Off to the Cathedral . . . not only to give thanks for the return of friends and neighbors, but to give thanks for a brave leader like Columbus, a worthy leader for Spain and for the world.

THE END

Fire in a Paper

Read *Fire in a Paper* silently. In this story some of the phrasing is unusual. Read the following phrases to yourself. If you do not know what they mean, talk them over together. Ask the teacher if you are in doubt.

Honorable mistress
Your esteemed daughters-in-law
forever running away to make merry
honored lady
unmindful of our duty
little pheasants
honorable mother of our husbands
our greatly-to-be-respected husbands
my feet could hardly wait
we have tarried too long
fresh kumquats
I am humbly grateful
delicious morsel

Now that you have had a chance to read these phrases to yourself and get their meaning, try reading them aloud. Each person should read one line. If it is not smooth and meaningful, try again.

1. Choose people for the parts in the play.
2. Practice reading together two or three times.
3. Help each other with difficult words, phrases, and voices.
4. Get ready to read your play to the class.

FIRE IN A PAPER

by Loleta Hagy

Characters

(4 girls, 1 woman, and the narrator)

NARRATOR
FOU CHOW, *the mistress*
LOTUS BLOSSOM, *a daughter-in-law*
MOON FLOWER, *another daughter-in-law*
SOOEY SAN, *a friend of the girls*
TIA, *a servant*

NARRATOR: The play that you are about to hear is based on an old legend. In a room in Fou Chow's home, Fou Chow is seated cross-legged on a pile of cushions. She is embroidering. Tia, a servant, appears at the door.

TIA: Honorable mistress, your esteemed daughters-in-law beg permission to speak to you.

FOU CHOW: Ah, perhaps they have brought me some delicacy, or a bit of silk with a new design on it. They are such charming and obedient daughters-in-law.

TIA: I think it is a request they have to make this time, most highly respected mistress.

FOU CHOW: A request? Can it be possible that they wish to go to visit their village again? It is but five days since they visited their parents, and before that was another five days. What? Are my daughters-in-law not satisfied with the home my sons have given them that they must be forever running away to make merry in their own village? They are, indeed, very stupid girls. Send them to me. I will find a way to stop this once and for all. . . . Well, my little Lotus Blossom, and you Moon Flower, since you come to me empty-handed, and it is not time to serve my tea, what request have you to make?

LOTUS BLOSSOM: It is true, honored lady, that today we bring no gifts, but it is not because we are unmindful of our duty to our dear mother-in-law. It was simply that the gifts we had were not worthy of so illustrious a personage. But if you will permit us to pay a visit to the village where we were born, we shall surely find something there worthy to present to you.

FOU CHOW: Yes, little pheasants, you may go and pay a visit to the old village. Go as soon as you like. But remember this —you must bring back to me, when you come, the only two things for which I have a desire in all the world, or you shall never again return to your homes or your husbands.

LOTUS BLOSSOM: Oh, we shall gladly bring you whatever you wish, honored lady.

FOU CHOW: Very well, then. You, Lotus Blossom, shall bring me fire wrapped in a paper, and you, Moon Flower, shall bring me some wind in a paper.

LOTUS BLOSSOM: Fire in a paper! How pretty!

MOON FLOWER: Wind in a paper! . . . Wind in a paper!

LOTUS BLOSSOM: You shall have them, honorable mother of our husbands.

NARRATOR: Now let's follow the girls to their village. Here we find them in the home of their friend, Sooey San. The three girls are eating bowls of sweet rice. They are using chopsticks. Let's listen to what they are saying.

LOTUS BLOSSOM: It is a new dance. Moon Flower learned it from a geisha.

SOOEY SAN: A geisha! Why, Moon Flower! Does your honorable mother-in-law know?

MOON FLOWER: Indeed no, Sooey San, nor our greatly-to-be-respected husbands. It was at the Feast of the Lanterns I saw the dance, and I carried it home in my head. My feet could hardly wait to be taught. Lotus Blossom knew the music and she helped me to learn the steps.

LOTUS BLOSSOM: Oh, Moon Flower. It is late. We must hurry or our honored lady will be very angry, to say nothing of our husbands.

MOON FLOWER: You are right, Lotus Blossom. We have tarried too long in the pleasant home of our friend. Goodbye, Sooey San.

LOTUS BLOSSOM: Oh, Moon Flower, have you forgotten the words of our honorable mother-in-law?

MOON FLOWER: That we must bring—bring—oh, what shall we do?

SOOEY SAN: Why do you weep, little friends?

LOTUS BLOSSOM: Oh, and who would not weep! We can never, never go to our pleasant home again.

MOON FLOWER: No, never, never. It is our mother-in-law's command.

SOOEY SAN: Stop crying, foolish ones, and tell me why you can never go home.

MOON FLOWER: Oh, Sooey San, my mother-in-law told me never to return unless I brought her a gift.

LOTUS FLOWER: And I, too.

SOOEY SAN: That is nothing to cry about. I have some fresh kumquats and some delicious preserve.

LOTUS BLOSSOM: She does not want them, Sooey San. Only two things in all the world she wants, and they are fire in a paper and wind in a paper. These we must bring her or never return.

SOOEY SAN: It seems she is punishing you for some ingratitude. Did she appear angry?

LOTUS BLOSSOM: I think she did not like us to come so often to our village.

SOOEY SAN: And she is quite right; your duty is in your home. You have been thoughtless and heedless, but come, let us put our heads together and we may find a way out of the matter.

NARRATOR: They are sitting silently in a circle. All have thoughtful frowns on their faces. Wait! Sooey San has jumped up and is taking down one of her beautiful paper lanterns. She hands it to Lotus Blossom.

LOTUS BLOSSOM: Ah, there you have it. The very thing for me to take back to my honored mother-in-law—fire wrapped in a paper.

NARRATOR: They are all sitting silently again. Suddenly, Lotus Blossom reaches for a paper fan and waves it before Moon Flower.

LOTUS BLOSSOM: See, Moon Flower, your fan. Take it and wave it back and forth before your face.

MOON FLOWER: Wind in a paper! Now I too may return home.

LOTUS BLOSSOM: We must be on our way. My humble thanks to you, Sooey San.

MOON FLOWER: I am humbly grateful to you both. Farewell, Sooey San. You have taught us a lesson. We have been very unmindful of the patience of our most highly respected husbands and of our mother-in-law. In the future, no matter how sadly our hearts cry for our own village, we shall make ourselves content to stay at home.

NARRATOR: It is tea time at the home of Fou Chow. Tia brings in a tiny red lacquer table set with blue china, and places it before Fou Chow.

TIA: Honorable mistress, your daughters-in-law have returned and beg permission to enter.

FOU CHOW (*Astonished*): My daughters-in-law! Bid them enter.

NARRATOR: Lotus Blossom and Moon Flower enter meekly and bow low. They keep their gifts behind them.

FOU CHOW: Have there come to this family daughters-in-law who do not obey their mother-in-law? Have you come here without fire wrapped in a paper and wind in a paper?

LOTUS BLOSSOM: Nay, honored lady, I have done your bidding.

MOON FLOWER: And I also. Behold the gift I have brought— wind in a paper.

LOTUS BLOSSOM: And my gift—fire wrapped in paper.

FOU CHOW (*Pleased*): Well, at last you have done some thinking. Come serve me with tea. . . . Lotus Blossom, hang the gay lantern above our table that it may add to our pleasure. Did you have a pleasurable visit to your village, little pheasants?

LOTUS BLOSSOM: Most enjoyable, honorable mother, but the homes of our friends are not so delightful as this one, nor so desirable.

MOON FLOWER: In the future, we shall leave our home with greatest reluctance. Will you deign to taste some fresh kumquats that our friend Sooey San bid us bring to you, and some delicious preserve?

FOU CHOW: Ah, delicious morsel. I must go frequently to the village where such delightful fruit can be had. You shall go with me, little pigeons, when I go, to help me choose. Would you like that?

THE END

You have now read many plays. Try to do this one without any special practice.

1. Read the play to yourself. Ask each other for help as you read. Notice the voice directions.
2. Decide together some of the things you think you will have to do to read this play well. Have your chairman jot them down on the blackboard or on paper.
   Decide together who will take each part.
3. Practice reading the play aloud once or twice.
4. Pause and give extra practice to those parts that need it.
5. Try reading the play through from beginning to end *once more*.
6. Tell your teacher when you are ready and arrange to read it to the class.

THE LITTLEST MONTH

by Damally Faux

Characters

(1 man, 8 boys, 4 girls, and the narrator)

NARRATOR

FATHER TIME, *an old, old, man who controls the seasons*

THE TWELVE MONTHS, *the twelve months of the year*

NARRATOR: Today we are going to visit the court of Father Time. It is a very long time ago. We find Father Time seated on his throne talking with his twelve months.

FATHER TIME: Be seated, ye seasons, and mark what I say. For a long time now I have thought the world should have more order. Man never knows when one of you will decide to overstay your time. Some of you actually bring your weather out of season. This must stop. (*In a loud voice*) April, stop your laughing.

APRIL: Yes, Father Time . . . Boo hoo . . . Boooo hooooo. . . .

FATHER TIME: April, I do declare. One never knows which side of you to believe.

MAY: She always smiles for me, Father Time.

MARCH (*Roars*): Well, I can make her cry!

FEBRUARY (*Gently*): But March, you are so strong you frighten her.

FATHER TIME: Enough. Enough, I say! Listen to my plan. All the year will be divided into days and you shall each share alike.

JANUARY: But, Father Time, that cannot be. There are 365 days in a year and only twelve of us.

FATHER TIME: I have a plan to divide the year.

JANUARY: But, Father Time, we all can't have equal days. So, I shall take the extra five because I am the beginning of the year.

MARCH: Indeed you won't. As it is, I have to keep my March winds in my bag too long. No, I shall have the extra days. I must sail the ships and fly the kites and carry the rain for April, even though she never smiles at me.

APRIL: I bring the April showers, so surely I should have the extra days.

MAY: But all the orchards bloom in May and much of the planting is done by me. Surely I should have the extra days.

JULY: Of course you all know everyone would like me to stay for the whole year.

JUNE: No, no, no. . . .

JANUARY: No, no, no. . . .

AUGUST: Well, I think we should take only our share, but we summer months *are* the most popular, you know.

SEPTEMBER: Of course I should like to have more days as I find my time is all too short at the first and far too long at the end. (*Thoughtfully*) Perhaps some arrangement could be made not to stop the vacations in September; that's given me such a bad name.

OCTOBER: Well, nobody doubts that October is the most beautiful. I could well afford to stay longer than the rest.

NOVEMBER: There is so much harvesting to be done. Can you think of a better way to use those extra days than for gathering the crops in November?

DECEMBER: How foolish you all are. It is very plain to me that Christmastime should last the entire year. I have often heard people wish for it.

JANUARY: I still say I should have the extra days.

FEBRUARY: No, my good friends, this is no way to settle the matter. Let us all give a day and agree we cannot use Father Time this way.

JANUARY: I for one will not give up.

MARCH: Nor I.

MAY: I should love to, but I simply can't.

JUNE: May, you mean you will not.

JULY: Well, I won't withdraw.

AUGUST: Nor will I.

OCTOBER: No one would want me to, so I won't.

DECEMBER: Well, as I said before, everybody wants me to last all year, so of course I shan't give in.

FEBRUARY: Then will you take thirty days, April?

APRIL: Yes, February, if you ask it.

JUNE: I am very lucky. I have most of the weddings and roses. I can well afford to be generous.

SEPTEMBER: I represent the month of learning, so of course I can compromise, only I do wish I were not so unpopular with the children.

NOVEMBER: I have so much to be grateful for. I will take the thirty days and fill them with Thanksgiving.

FEBRUARY: Are there then no others who will give up days to

make the months come out even? We cannot all lay claim to the extra five days. Let two of you give up your claims and then the others may each have an extra day.

OCTOBER: No, no. . . .

JULY: No, no. . . .

FEBRUARY: Then, for the sake of peace, I shall give up two of my own days.

NOVEMBER: No, no, February, you should not do that.

FEBRUARY: It is the only way. But I shall make the most of my twenty-eight days.

NARRATOR: Poor old Father Time. He has been having a hard time keeping awake. He opens his eyes suddenly.

FATHER TIME: What! What! Twenty-eight days? Who said twenty-eight days?

FEBRUARY: I did, Father Time. The months have all agreed to take thirty or thirty-one days. It is all arranged.

FATHER TIME: I declare! How can it be? I was here all the time.

FEBRUARY: So you were, Father Time, but you slipped away again. We thought to save you and this is our plan.

JANUARY: January has thirty-one days in which to skate and ski and ride on sleighs. I make the earth hard and cold and cover it with snow.

MARCH: March has thirty-one days and I will blow and blow.

APRIL: April has thirty days, Father Time.

MAY: May has thirty-one days in which to strew the earth with blossoms.

JUNE: I took thirty days for June.

JULY (*In a sleepy voice*): I took thirty-one days for July.

AUGUST: Of course August had to have thirty-one days.

SEPTEMBER: I reached the decision, Father Time, that I would take only thirty days, in order to make peace . . . but I still wish you could do something to make September more popular.

OCTOBER: Naturally October must have thirty-one.

NOVEMBER: I am very grateful for my full thirty days of November.

DECEMBER: You understand, Father Time, that I had to have my thirty-one December days.

FATHER TIME: Had you, indeed? Then February, you have only twenty-eight days. Well, I'll make up for that. Every four years you shall have an extra day. Then . . . there should be something else for you, February . . . Oh, yes, I have it. For your generosity, you shall be unlike the other months in many ways. Just twenty-eight days and an extra day every four years and in your month our greatest citizens will be born. I shall take you into the future. February twelfth, Abraham Lincoln shall be born. And on February fourteenth . . . we will make that a happy day of love—Valentine's Day. On February twenty-second there will be born a great leader of men—George Washington. And now, you months must do your work. I wish to return to the ages.

THE END

The Heroine of Wren

This play is longer than many you have read so far. Read it silently and try to get the meaning of the story. Try to imagine how you would feel if you were the Halls and had to leave your home. Think of how you might feel if you were Colonel Day and read the note left by Cynthia.

What words can you think of to describe Grandfather Hall? What kind of voice would he have?

How would you describe Cynthia?

What words would you use to describe her voice? Would it change? How?

Can you think of some words to describe Colonel Day?

What kind of voice do you think he might have? Would he sound the same when he was talking to himself as when he was talking to his orderly? How would you describe the change?

1. Decide together who might be best for each part.
2. Practice reading the play.
3. Go over it until:
   You are reading without hesitation.
   Everyone comes in on time.
   Every word in the play can be heard and understood.
4. Plan with your teacher the best time to read it to the class.

THE HEROINE OF WREN

by Ella Stratton Colbo

Characters

(1 girl, 1 woman, 4 men, and the narrator)

NARRATOR

CYNTHIA HALL, *a little girl who lives with her grandfather. She is not afraid to ask people to be kind.*

GRANDMOTHER HALL, *an old lady who has lost sons in the war and is now fearful of losing her home*

GRANDFATHER HALL, *an old man who is also worried and fearful of losing his home*

A RIDER, *a young man who rides through the village to warn the people to leave quickly*

COLONEL DAY, *the head of the English forces*

AN ORDERLY, *the colonel's servant*

NARRATOR: Our play today takes place during the American Revolution. Here in a simple Quaker cottage in the village of Wren we find Grandmother Hall working about. Her grandchild, Cynthia, has just run into the room. She is very excited.

CYNTHIA: Oh, Grandmother, Grandmother, the Redcoats are coming! A rider on horseback is at Neighbor Randall's telling them about it. I was bringing their morning pail of milk to them for Grandfather, and I heard the rider say we must all leave the village and flee for our lives.

GRANDMOTHER: I have no doubt the rider will soon be here to tell Grandfather all about it, so do thou run to the barn and tell him to come quickly. But first dry thy tears, Cynthia, like the brave little maid thou art. Thy grandfather is an old man. Since thy father and his brothers fell at Brandywine he has had naught but trouble, and this will be the worst of all. We must both be brave, and try not to make it harder for him.

CYNTHIA: I will, Grandmother. I will! Grandfather shall not see me cry.

GRANDMOTHER: That's my own brave little maid. Now run to call him. There is no time to lose.

NARRATOR: As Grandmother starts her work again, she is startled by the voice of the Rider.

RIDER (*Urgently*): Mistress Hall? I *must* have speech with thy husband, at *once*.

GRANDMOTHER: He is coming from the barn, sir. Here he is now.

RIDER: I am sorry, good sir, to be the bearer of bad tidings this fine morning, but I am sent to warn all the villagers that they must gather up what food they can, and flee to the hills at once. The Redcoats are less than a day's march to the westward, plundering and pillaging as they come. They are likely to camp in this village tonight. Make ready to leave with all possible haste. Neighbor Randall will stop for you presently, bringing two horses that you may ride. Remember, for safety's sake, you must all be in the hills by nightfall!

GRANDFATHER: Thank you kindly, sir. We will make ready to leave at once.

RIDER: Now I must hasten to warn the others.

GRANDMOTHER: I will bring thee the good silver from the chest in the bedroom, and do thou dig a hole in the garden to bury it where the Redcoats will not think to look. Cynthia, child, run to find an old sack to wrap it well.

GRANDFATHER: Yes, Cynthia, lass, thou must lend thy willing hands and quick feet this day to spare thy Grandmother's strength for the sad times ahead. Since our own lads have given their lives for their country, thou art all we have left. Grandmother is old, and I fear that tonight she will look down from the hills to see the sky reddened with the fires of our burning homes.

CYNTHIA: I will do my very best . . . but oh, Grandfather, even the *Redcoats* couldn't be *that* cruel!

GRANDMOTHER: Here is the silver. I found a sack to wrap it. Do thou hide it quickly.

GRANDFATHER: Don't thee worry. I will find a safe hiding place for thy treasure, and then I will give Old Bess a last good feeding. Mayhap the Redcoats will not harm her if she gives them plenty of her good milk for supper.

GRANDMOTHER: We have much to do before Neighbor Randall

calls for us. Cynthia lass, run to the kitchen and pack the market basket with the corn cakes, and whatever else is left of yesterday's food. Take all thee can find. We will not care to light fires to cook our supper tonight. Hurry, child. I will busy myself packing what little we may be able to take with us.

CYNTHIA: Burn our home! Harm Old Bess! If the Redcoats only knew how good and kind Grandmother and Grandfather are . . . how old and helpless . . . and that no one is left in all this world to care for them but a little girl, they could not be so cruel and heartless. I *know!* I will write them a note, and ask them to spare this house . . . this whole *village*. It can do no harm, and it may do some good. . . . To the Redcoats . . . Gentlemen: . . . Please. . . .

NARRATOR: Cynthia writes busily. She finishes her note and puts it in her pocket. She leaves the room. Where is she going to put the note? Here is Grandmother. She is carrying two parcels. There are two cloaks over her arm.

GRANDMOTHER: There . . . I do not dare to take time for more . . . besides, we could carry little else. (*Calls loudly*) Cynthia!

GRANDFATHER: Make ready quickly. I can see the villagers beginning to come down the road.

GRANDMOTHER: Cynthia! Come lass, we must start at once.

CYNTHIA: Grandmother, Grandfather! What about the geese? If I open the gate to their pen, they might go to the woods and be safe, too. I simply couldn't *bear* to have anything happen to my pet gander, Nicodemus!

GRANDMOTHER: Run and open the gate to their pen, if it will make thee any happier; but geese are silly things, lass, and they are sure to come back home at nightfall, Redcoats or no Redcoats. Hurry then, and meet us at the front gate.

NARRATOR: Grandmother and Grandfather go out the front door. Cynthia hastily scribbles a few more lines on the bottom of the paper, refolds it and places it against the candlesticks on the table. Grandfather calls for her to hurry.

GRANDFATHER: Cynthia, Cynthia! Neighbor Randall is waiting for thee!

CYNTHIA: Coming, Grandfather!

NARRATOR: And now a bit later at the little cottage we find the British Colonel Day and his orderly.

COLONEL: I like the looks of this cottage. It shall be my headquarters while we are camped in the village of Wren. Post two guards outside the door. I am both hungry and weary. Give the cook orders to get supper under way immediately. . . . Ho! what have we here? A message "To the Redcoats," as I live! . . . (*Reads slowly and loudly*) "Gentlemen: My name is Cynthia Hall. I live in this house with my good, kind grandmother and grandfather. It is the only home we have. I beg of you not to burn our home, or harm Old Bess, our cow. We would freeze and starve when the cold winter comes. We need our garden, too, and dear Grandmother loves her flowers. Please, sirs, if you have little daughters of your own, think how they would cry if harm came to their homes. We have done you no harm. Have pity on my poor grandparents, and mercy on the village of Wren. Respectfully yours, Mistress Cynthia Hall. P.S. I have just let our geese out of their pens, but they are silly things and will come home at nightfall, Redcoats or no Redcoats. Nicodemus, the gander, is my very own pet. I love him dearly. I could not bear to lose Nicodemus" (*Laughs heartily*) Ho, ho! Written bravely enough, little Mistress Hall! Methinks my own little Cynthia at home would be as quick to speak up spunkily for her rights if danger threatened. Orderly! Take this command to Captain Flynn, and have him make it known to all the men. Tell him there is to be absolutely no pillage or plunder this night. They are to take only what is needed for one good meal for men and animals . . . and leave everything else unharmed . . . *everything*, understand! Tell them I am doing this as a favor to a brave little rebel lass, who asked it in the name of our own little daughters in faraway England. At dawn we will march on, leaving the village as we found it.

ORDERLY: Very well, sir.

COLONEL: Just as she said! Geese *are* silly things! Here they all come, single file, with Nicodemus himself in the lead! I fear the cook will covet those plump fowls for our supper, but they shall spare your pet, I promise you, Mistress Cynthia! We will have a good meal, and a good night's rest, and at dawn we will march away, leaving the village of Wren as we found it. I must go to the kitchen. I have business with the cook . . . about Nicodemus!

NARRATOR: It is the next day. Cynthia, Grandmother, and Grandfather are coming back. Cynthia is helping Grandmother.

GRANDMOTHER (*Wonderingly*): Why, look thee, lass! Nothing is really harmed. Nothing is broken or spoiled! Not a thing! And a good scrubbing with soap and water will make quick work of all these muddy tracks on the floor. We have much to be thankful for, my child.

GRANDFATHER: The whole village is rejoicing! Nothing has been harmed! Nothing has been taken but food! God hath indeed wrought a miracle for the village of Wren! Our garden is the same as we left it . . . not even a flower has been trampled. And Old Bess is contentedly chewing her cud in the barn!

GRANDMOTHER: What is this? It looks like a letter. It is! With Cynthia's name written upon it. Read it, child. Read it aloud.

CYNTHIA: "To a Brave Little Rebel Lass: You could not have known it when you wrote your note, begging us to spare your grandfather's home, and the village of Wren, but I *do* have a little Cynthia of my own in faraway England to whom I would wish no harm to come. Therefore, with the compliments of Mistress Cynthia Day, your request is granted. My kindest regards, Colonel Day." Grandfather, have you looked for our geese? Is Nicodemus safe? . . .

There he is! Walking about all alone. They must have eaten all the others.

GRANDFATHER: Yes. He is all alone, and the gate is closed again.

GRANDMOTHER: Whatever can that be tied about his neck? It looks like a small sack. It looks heavy. It swings back and forth as he walks. Run outside, lass, and see what it is. Do thou bring it here.

GRANDFATHER: So *that* is the story! It is to our little Cynthia that the whole village of Wren owes its thanks!

GRANDMOTHER: Aye, we may well be proud of our little lass this day. She has served her country bravely and well. But here she comes. . . .

CYNTHIA: Look, look! A whole sackful of coins! And another note from the Redcoats! Listen to this!

> Dear Mistress Cynthia:
> We have eaten your geese,
> But not to be rude!
> We were tired and hungry,
> We had to have food.
>
> We each leave, in payment,
> A coin with your pet.
> You said we were gentlemen. . . .
> We will not forget!

GRANDFATHER: A goodly sum, indeed!

GRANDMOTHER: We can buy many, many things with all these coins!

CYNTHIA: And *I* have Nicodemus. Oh, I am so happy!

GRANDFATHER: Thy grandmother and I are proud of thee, this day, little maid. Thee is a *real heroine!*

THE END

Miss Muffet's Wish

When you have read *Miss Muffet's Wish* to yourself and understand what it is all about, practice the following exercises:
Read these lines and see if you pause properly at the dots. Sometimes they indicate an unfinished sentence. At other times they show an interruption. They also show pauses.

JERRY: How'd you get in here?
BARBARA: Through the gate. It was open and. . . .
JERRY: Oh. Trespassing!
BARBARA: Oh, no! I. . . .
JERRY: You can't come in here. This is private property. It belongs to Mr. Hansen.
BARBARA: Yes, I know. My daddy used to work for him, but . . . but he was fired.
JERRY: Where do you live?
BARBARA: On Elm Street. . . . That's a tuffet, isn't it?

Did the pauses sound natural?
Were they too long? Too short?
Did they help the meaning of the story?
Let two other people try the same lines.
Get ready to read together.

1. Choose your parts.
2. Read the play together.
3. Decide where you need more practice.
4. Work on those parts again.
5. Read the whole play again.
6. Decide whether you need to work longer. If so, you know what to do.

7. When you are satisfied with yourselves prepare to read the play to the other children.

MISS MUFFET'S WISH

by Robert St. Clair

Characters

(2 girls, 1 boy, 1 man, and the narrator)

NARRATOR
JERRY, *a boy who likes to work with flowers and plants*
JERRY'S FATHER, *the gardener on a large estate*
BARBARA, *a little girl whose father lost his position. She wants to make a wish come true.*
ALICE, *a little girl whose father owns the big estate*

NARRATOR: Today's play takes us to the lovely lawn near a big house. Here we meet Jerry, the gardener's son. Jerry is very busy trimming the grass around a tree. Listen. Jerry's father is calling to him.

JERRY'S FATHER: Jerry! Oh, Jerry!

JERRY (*Calling*): Here I am, Pa.

JERRY'S FATHER: What are you doing?

JERRY (*Calling*): Cutting the grass around this tree.

JERRY'S FATHER: Getting to be quite a helper, aren't you, son?

JERRY (*Proudly*): I'm going to be a gardener *too* when *I* grow up. Say, who can this be? Oh, some silly girl with her nose in a book. Girls always have their noses in books. Doesn't even know where she is, I bet.

BARBARA: "Little Miss Muffet sat on a tuffet,
    Eating of curds and whey:
    Along came a spider,
    And sat down beside her,
    And frightened Miss Muffet away."
Oh, hello!

JERRY: Hello, yourself. How'd you get in here?

BARBARA: Through the gate. It was open and. . . .

JERRY: Oh. Trespassing!

BARBARA: Oh, no. I. . . .

JERRY: You can't come in here. Don't you know this is private property? (*Importantly*) It belongs to Mr. Hansen.

BARBARA: Yes, I know. My daddy used to work for him, but . . . but he was fired. Who are you?

JERRY: I'm the head gardener's son. We live in a cottage back of the big house. Where do you live?

BARBARA: On Elm Street. . . . That's a tuffet, isn't it?

JERRY: A what?

BARBARA: Underneath that tree. A tuffet is like a little hill or mound. That's what I came here for . . . to sit on the tuffet under the trees and make a wish. Are there any spiders in that tree?

JERRY: Say! Are you crazy or something?

BARBARA (*Insistently*): Are there?

JERRY: I guess so. Why?

BARBARA: I want to make a wish.

JERRY (*Irritably*): What're you talking about anyway?

BARBARA (*Explaining*): You see, my name's Muffet . . . Barbara Muffet . . . just like the girl in the nursery rhyme. But I'm not as afraid of spiders as *she* was.

JERRY (*Sarcastically*): Oh, you're not, eh?

BARBARA: Not a bit. I like them. They bring you luck. My daddy says so.

JERRY: I suppose he knows all about it?

BARBARA (*Proudly*): My daddy knows everything.

JERRY: He didn't know enough to keep his job with Mr. Hansen, did he?

BARBARA: He had trouble with the foreman, not with Mr. Hansen.

JERRY: Why doesn't he get another job?

BARBARA: He can't. Every place he tries is full. He's so worried. That's why I got up enough courage to come in here.

I've got to let a spider come down in front of my face and then I'll make a wish. Then everything will be all right.

JERRY: I'll bet there are lots of spiders on Elm Street.

BARBARA: But there are no tuffets or trees, and in this picture, Miss Muffet is sitting on the grass under a tree . . . a tree just like that.

JERRY: You must believe in miracles.

BARBARA: Who's that?

JERRY: Who?

BARBARA: That girl on the porch.

JERRY: That's Alice, Mr. Hansen's only child.

BARBARA: I'll bet she'd be awfully nice to play with.

JERRY'S FATHER: Jerry! Come here.

JERRY: Yes, Pa. Better get going, Barbara. If Pa sees you, he'll tell you to get off the place.

BARBARA: I'll go as soon as I've made my wish.

JERRY: You'll never get your dad's job back for him that way. Why don't you ask Mr. Hansen himself to take your dad back?

BARBARA: Daddy's tried and tried but Mr. Hansen won't even see him.

JERRY'S FATHER: Jerry!

JERRY (*Calling*): I'm coming, Pa. Barbara, you're a crazy girl . . . but go ahead and get it over with.

BARBARA (*Eagerly*): Thanks. You're awfully nice.

JERRY (*Worriedly*): But if my Pa or Alice sees you, you'd better run. What do you want, Pa?

JERRY'S FATHER: Come on home and wash up for supper.

BARBARA: I'll just sit on this tuffet under the tree. Oh, there is a spider up there . . . a great big one . . . I can *see* him! (*Coaxingly*) Come on down, Mr. Spider. Please come down and help my daddy find work. It's awfully important. He's so unhappy . . . that spider won't even budge. "Little Miss Muffet sat on a tuffet, eating of curds and whey. . . ." Maybe I ought to have some cereal—hot cereal. That's the same as curds and whey. "Along came a spider and sat down beside her. . . ." Oh! he's coming! I must sit still. I mustn't even breathe!

ALICE: Well!

BARBARA: Shhhh! Don't speak.

ALICE: Who are you?

BARBARA: Don't come any closer. You'll scare him away.

ALICE: Who?

BARBARA (*In a loud half-whisper*): The spider.

ALICE: Ohhhh.

BARBARA (*Eagerly*): Now he's moving again! He's coming closer and closer!

ALICE: Be careful!

BARBARA (*Breathlessly*): Look! He's on my hand! It's time to wish! Please give my daddy his job back. . . . OUCH! He bit me!

ALICE: Oh! Goodness! That's a *black widow* spider! And he bit you!

NARRATOR: Poor Barbara. Of course Alice called for help. Mr. Hansen came and carried Barbara up to Alice's bedroom. That's where we find them now. Barbara has been asleep.

ALICE (*Cheerfully*): Hello. Are you awake?

BARBARA: Where . . . where am I?

ALICE: In my bedroom. Daddy brought you here.

BARBARA: Mr. Hansen?

ALICE: That's right. You fainted after the spider bit you. You've been unconscious for several hours. We've had the doctor and everything.

BARBARA: Am I . . . am I going to die?

ALICE: Of course not. The doctor says that black widows are not poisonous at this time of the year. But he gave you some medicine.

BARBARA: I must go home. Mother and Daddy will be worried.

ALICE: No. You've got to stay here all night. Your folks know. Daddy told them. They're here now.

BARBARA (*Amazed*): Here?

ALICE: Downstairs . . . talking about your father's new job.

BARBARA (*Dazedly*): New . . . job?

ALICE: Yes. You see, you were delirious, and my, how you talked! You told us why you came here, who you were and everything. Daddy felt terribly sorry. He's going to give your father a good job now.

BARBARA (*Happily*): Then the wish did come true!

ALICE: I guess it did.

BARBARA: But I'm never going to try it again.

ALICE: You're not?

BARBARA: Not with spiders. You see, I'm like the real Miss Muffet now and spiders frighten me to death!

THE END

A Needle Fights for Freedom

This is the story of Betsy Ross and how she came to make the first flag. It is a story you have all heard before.

There are no difficult words or phrases to bother you. See if you can prepare your play in a different way today.

Read the page that tells you who the different characters are. Decide which part each will take.

Try your own part over to yourself. Ask for help on any words you do not know. Watch the punctuation. Think what kind of voice you should use.

Now try reading the play together.

First think about all the things you have learned.

1. Come in promptly with your lines.
2. Use your voice to express surprise, impatience, command, etc.
3. Speak clearly and distinctly and not too rapidly.
4. Try to sound real! Make the things in the play really happen.

Practice together until you feel that you are ready to read for others. Help one another whenever you need to.

Plan with your teacher the best time to read to your class.

A NEEDLE FIGHTS FOR FREEDOM

by Esther MacLellan and Catherine V. Schroll

Characters

(5 girls, 1 woman, 3 men, and the narrator)

NARRATOR

PEGGY
CONSTANCE
ELIZABETH *girls in Betsy Ross' sewing class. Peggy is the*
ANNE *impatient one. She finds sewing rather dull.*
PRUE

MISTRESS BETSY ROSS, *known as the most skillful needlewoman in Philadelphia*

GENERAL WASHINGTON

ROBERT MORRIS *two men who come to the home of Betsy*
COLONEL ROSS *Ross with the general*

NARRATOR: It is the year 1776 and we are about to look in on the home of Betsy Ross in Philadelphia. We find five girls having a sewing lesson.

ANNE: There! I've pricked my finger again! Ow! Mean old needle.

PRUE: My grandmother says we should be glad that Mistress Betsy Ross is teaching us to sew.

PEGGY: Well, I'm tired of sitting still. I wish I were a boy. Then I'd go to war.

PRUE: You're not big enough.

PEGGY: I'm big enough to play a drum.

ANNE: It would be more fun than sewing.

PEGGY: Of course it would. And you'd be helping our country, too. My father says that everybody should fight for freedom. How can one fight for freedom with a needle, Mistress Ross?

BETSY ROSS: Maybe you can't fight with a needle, Peggy, and maybe you can.

PEGGY: Fight with a needle? How would a needle have helped our soldiers at Bunker Hill?

BETSY ROSS: By making them warm clothes, of course. The British laugh at the rags some of our boys must wear. They call them an army of beggars.

PEGGY: But I'm just sewing an old seam. I can't make clothes.

BETSY ROSS: And you never will be able to make clothes unless you first learn on small things. A baby crawls before it walks, you know. Let's see, girls, show me your work. . . . Very nice, Prue. A little crooked, Anne. Peggy, your stitches are much too large.

PEGGY: I wish they were even larger. Then I'd be finished.

BETSY ROSS: This kind of work only takes longer, Peggy. Now, you must rip out your seam and do it over.

PEGGY: Again?

BETSY ROSS: Again and again, until it's right. I must go to the kitchen. I'll be back in a moment, girls. Keep sewing.

CONSTANCE: That's a shame, Peggy.

PEGGY: I suppose it's my own fault. (*Sighing*) I did hurry.

PRUE: Those great big stitches of yours would pull out in a minute.

PEGGY: Oh, dear! If I were only helping in the fight for freedom instead of just sewing. How I would love to do something for General Washington, something he really needs!

ELIZABETH: Cheer up, Peggy. Maybe you can sew him a shirt when you learn to make smaller stitches.

PEGGY (*Impatiently*): A shirt! I mean something for *America*.

PRUE: I think I heard someone knock. Shall I answer the door?

ANNE: Why not? Mistress Ross is busy in the kitchen.

PEGGY: If it's a poor beggar, I'll gladly give him my needle.

WASHINGTON: Is this the home of Mistress Betsy Ross?

PRUE: Yes, sir.

PEGGY: Anne! Anne! That's General Washington!

ANNE: You must be mistaken, Peggy.

PEGGY: Indeed I am not! Oh, sir, you *are* General Washington, aren't you?

WASHINGTON: I am, my little maid.

PEGGY: But what are you doing here, sir? I thought you were busy. . . .

WASHINGTON: I am busy.

PEGGY: Excuse me, sir, I didn't mean you weren't. But I meant busy galloping at the head of the army.

WASHINGTON: We don't gallop all the time, my dear.

MR. MORRIS: Come, come, child. Where is Mistress Ross?

CONSTANCE: I'll get her, sir.

MR. MORRIS: Are you sure that Mistress Ross will be able to do what we want?

WASHINGTON: I've heard that she is a fine needlewoman.

ELIZABETH: Oh, sir, she is. Mistress Ross sews better than anyone in Philadelphia.

BETSY ROSS: General Washington! I am honored, sir. What can I do for you?

WASHINGTON: Mistress Ross, this is Mr. Robert Morris and this is Colonel Ross.

MR. MORRIS: Your servant, ma'am.

COLONEL ROSS: A pleasure, ma'am.

WASHINGTON: We have come to ask you to do something important, Mistress Ross, something for your country.

PEGGY: Is Mistress Ross to fight, sir? Is she to be in the army?

ELIZABETH: Peggy, be quiet, do. General Washington will be angry.

WASHINGTON: Angry? No, not I. I have a liking for little maids. But Peggy, there are other ways to serve your country than by fighting. Mistress Ross can help us with her needle.

COLONEL ROSS: Madam, our country needs a flag.

MR. MORRIS: Now that we are fighting England, we can no longer use the English flag that once we loved so well.

COLONEL ROSS: We must have a flag of our own, one that will stir the hearts of all our citizens.

WASHINGTON: Exactly. Some of our men march under the pine trees of Massachusetts. . . .

MR. MORRIS: Others under the banner of a rattlesnake, divided into thirteen parts.

WASHINGTON: We need *one* flag, one for everybody . . . a flag which will make our people realize that they are no more a part of old England, but a new country.

MR. MORRIS: And a free country, General Washington, where all men are joined together under one great flag.

BETSY ROSS: I shall do my best, gentlemen.

WASHINGTON: I am sure of it. These are our plans. What do you think of this?

BETSY ROSS: Beautiful, General Washington. I love the colors; red, white and blue.

MR. MORRIS: A stripe and a star for each of the thirteen colonies.

BETSY ROSS: This is the six-pointed star of the old flag. Let's have one of our own, a new star for our new country. What do you say to a five-pointed star?

WASHINGTON: Would it be difficult to make?

BETSY ROSS: Not in the least, sir. Peggy, give me your seam, my child. . . . I'll cut it . . . so. . . . How do you like it, General Washington?

WASHINGTON: Very much. Mistress Ross, we will leave the plan with you.

BETSY ROSS: I shall start at once.

WASHINGTON: Good!

MR. MORRIS: Work fast, Mistress Ross. Our country needs its flag.

WASHINGTON: It does indeed. Farewell, Mistress Ross. Goodbye, my dears. If you learn to sew as well as your good teacher, perhaps one day your needles may serve our country, too.

BETSY ROSS: Goodbye, gentlemen.

PEGGY: To think my ugly old seam was changed into a star— the first star of our new flag!

ELIZABETH: Perhaps you'll feel different about sewing now, Peggy.

PRUE: You see that in serving your country a needle can be just as important as a drumstick.

CONSTANCE: And I say that the needle that makes a flag is a needle that fights for freedom!

PEGGY (*Slowly*): Well, I suppose you're right, Constance, though I still think that beating a drum is lots more exciting. Even if I'm not very good at sewing, I'm terribly proud of my teacher.

BETSY ROSS: Thank you, Peggy. Sewing class is over, girls. On with your bonnets. My other work must be put aside. Now, this very minute, I start . . . I start to make our first American flag!

THE END

What He Deserves

Read the play silently. See if you can answer these questions.

Why did the Peasant bring a gift to the King?

Why did the Rich Man bring a gift to the King?

What was the Rich Man's reward?

Why did the Queen feel he got what he deserved?

Use these lines and let different boys try them. Choose the best reader for the part of the King. Remember—*be* a King, *act like* a King, *sound like* a King.

> KING: Such a gift is deserving of a reward. What shall we give him?

> KING: Page, bring me a bag of *gold* and *jewels*. We have decided to *reward* you, my honest man. Here is a bag of *gold* and *jewels* in return for your thought of us.

Use the following lines for the Peasant tryout. Choose the one who reads them best. Be humble and grateful. Show it in your voice and posture.

> PEASANT: Your Majesty, I am but a poor peasant, but when I harvested my turnips I found one *so large* it would *scarcely* go into my cart! I said to my wife, "Why, this is a *turnip* fit for a *king!*"

> PEASANT: Oh, thank you, Your Majesties! I can scarcely believe my good fortune.

1. Decide who is going to take the other parts.
2. Read your part over to yourself.
3. Practice reading together. Keep at it until you are satisfied that you are reading well.
4. Arrange for a time when you can read to the entire class.

WHAT HE DESERVES

by Helen L. Howard

Characters

(*5 men, 1 boy, 1 woman, and the narrator*)

NARRATOR

KING
QUEEN } *the rulers of the land*

PAGE, *a boy who serves the King*

PEASANT, *a poor man who has a farm*

PEASANT'S RICH BROTHER

TWO GUARDS, *soldiers who guard the castle*

NARRATOR: A King, much loved by his people, is seated in the throne room. There is a guard at each side of the throne. The King is talking with his Queen, who sits beside him.

KING: How good it is to be at peace again. Our country prospers and our people seem happy.

QUEEN: Our people are thankful to you for your leadership. The presents you are constantly receiving prove this.

KING: I am grateful to them for their tokens of affection. Page, you seem to be in a hurry. Do you have a message? Does someone seek justice?

PAGE: No, Sire. A peasant comes with a gift for you.

QUEEN: Even the peasants bring gifts!

KING: Let him come in that I may thank him in person. . . . My Queen, another gift. How pleasing to have even the peasants so generous!

PAGE: Here is the giver, Your Majesty.

KING: My page tells me that you have brought me a gift. I am very pleased with your thought of me.

PEASANT: Your Majesty, I am but a poor peasant, but when I harvested my turnips I found one so large that it would scarcely go into my cart. I said to my wife, "Why, this is a turnip fit for a king!" So, Your Majesty, I have brought it to you.

KING: A turnip larger than a cart! Where is this wonderful vegetable?

PEASANT: It is in the courtyard, Sire. It would scarcely go through the gate.

QUEEN: Let us see this remarkable turnip!

PEASANT: If you will look through the window, you can see it in the courtyard.

KING: Look! I have never seen such a sight before! It is indeed larger than a cart.

QUEEN: The cart is bending with its weight. It is a load even for two strong horses.

PEASANT: Yes, Your Majesty. My one horse could not draw it, so I borrowed one of my neighbor's horses.

KING: Such a gift is deserving of a reward. What shall we give him?

QUEEN: A bag of gold and jewels would help him most, no doubt.

KING: Page, bring me a bag of gold and jewels. We have decided to reward you, my honest man. Here is a bag of gold and jewels in return for your thought of us.

PEASANT: Oh, thank you, Your Majesties! I can scarcely believe my good fortune. Why, there is enough here to buy food and clothing for my good wife and me for the rest of our lives. You are most generous! I must be off to tell my wife.

QUEEN: Guard, follow that peasant but do not let him see you.

NARRATOR: It is now a few minutes later. The guard is hiding himself by a clump of bushes watching the peasant.

GUARD: Here comes the peasant now. I'll just hide here and wait until he passes; then I can follow him.

PEASANT: A whole bag of gold and jewels! After I pay my neighbor for his horse, I will still have more gold and jewels than I ever dreamed of.

NARRATOR: As the peasant is looking at his riches, his rich brother approaches. He is walking with his nose in the air. The rich brother bumps into the peasant, drops his cane and his high hat, but recovers his balance without falling down.

RICH BROTHER (*Angrily*): Here, you peasant! Why don't you look where you are going? Must we always be annoyed by you peasants walking along the same road with us!

PEASANT: Oh, sir, I'm sorry!

RICH MAN: Well, if it isn't my poor brother! Where have you been in your ragged coat?

PEASANT: I've been to the palace.

RICH MAN: To the PALACE! What have you been to the palace for? I suppose the King sent you a special invitation!

PEASANT: I took the King a present. Just see what he gave me in return.

RICH MAN: A bag of gold and jewels! What in the world did you give him that he made you such a present?

PEASANT: I gave him a turnip.

RICH MAN: A turnip! You gave the King a turnip and he made you a rich man!

PEASANT: Yes. I must hurry home and tell my wife of our good fortune.

RICH MAN: Hah! The King is too generous! . . . I have an idea. If the King gives a bag of gold and jewels for a mere turnip, what would he give for a truly fine gift! Now let me see . . . what does the King like best of all? I have it . . . *horses!* The King dotes on his fine horses and spends a great deal of time at the royal stables! I'll sell all of my land and buy the King fine horses. Then we shall see who is the best-rewarded giver in the kingdom! No doubt the King will make me a noble . . . indeed the wealthiest noble in the land!

NARRATOR: The guard, you remember, has been listening.

GUARD: This is information for the Queen. I'll return to the palace and tell her.

NARRATOR: And now a few hours later back in the throne

110 *WHAT HE DESERVES*

room of the palace the guard is talking with the Queen. The King is looking out of the window. He sees something that interests him. Listen.

KING: What a sight meets my eyes! Just coming into the courtyard are a dozen of the finest horses I have seen. Can it be that someone is making me another gift?

GUARD: Your Majesty, my Queen, it is he, the rich man.

QUEEN: How quickly he has disposed of his land and purchased the horses! He is as eager as he is generous!

KING: Such a gift must be well rewarded. My Queen, you must think of a special gift for this man.

QUEEN: Yes, indeed! He shall have the gift he deserves!

PAGE: A fine gentleman desires to see you, Sire. He has brought you a gift.

KING: Bid him enter at once. Have you thought of a reward for him, my dear?

QUEEN: Yes, he shall have what he deserves!

RICH MAN: Your Majesty, I have brought you a gift.

KING: Can it be all of those splendid horses I saw coming into the courtyard just now!

RICH MAN: Yes, Your Majesty. I wanted to show you how much I esteem and admire you for your leadership.

KING: How pleased I am! I must look again upon those fine horses. Come, my Queen, you must see them before deciding upon a reward. . . . Such a fine lot of animals!

QUEEN: These fine horses must have cost a fortune. Just see how proudly they hold their heads!

KING: Now what shall we give him?

NARRATOR: The King and Queen talk quietly. The Queen speaks.

QUEEN: It is what he deserves!

KING: Of course. The very thing! How clever you are! My man, you shall have as a reward the most wonderful thing in my palace! Only this morning a peasant brought me the most wonderful turnip in the world. It is so large that it will scarcely fit into a cart and had to be drawn by two horses. In return I gave him a bag of gold and jewels!

RICH MAN (*Eagerly*): Yes, yes . . . Your Majesty.

KING: You shall have this turnip.

RICH MAN: Oh, thank you, Your . . . a turnip! You mean. . . .

KING: Yes, I mean that you shall have this wonderful vegetable.

RICH MAN: But . . . Your Majesty . . . I. . . .

KING: Say no more, my good fellow! Such a gift as yours is indeed worthy of the most wonderful thing in the whole kingdom.

RICH MAN: But, Your Highness, I sold all of my possessions and spent all of my money. . . .

KING: To bring me a present. Indeed you are the only one worthy to receive this most unusual reward! Guards, take him out and give him this wonderful turnip . . . he shall have the horses and the cart as well.

RICH MAN (*Protesting*): But, Your Majesty, please listen to me. I tell you that I. . . .

KING: Have never seen anything so wonderful . . . neither have I. And you are the only one to whom I would give it.

RICH MAN (*In despair*): I'm ruined! Yes, guards, I'm coming.

KING: My dear Queen, how clever of you to think of giving the fine gentleman what he deserves!

THE END

The Runaway Pirate

Although *The Runaway Pirate* is not a ghost story or a fairy tale, it *is* a story based on imagination and make-believe. Read it to yourself. Try to get the feeling of confusion the pirate must experience. See if you can understand the attitude of the men in the harbor.

This play has many rhyming lines in it. Don't let them get sing-song.

Read these lines all together.

Are you *really* a pirate? A man of the sea?
And you want for your crew men like *me?*
And like *me?*
Of *course*, and I'll teach you the *ways* of a *ship.*
That's *kind* of you brother. We *need* a good *tip.*

Choose four boys and practice the following lines to see how promptly you come in.

PIRATE: It can hardly be seen.
OFFICER: It's well camouflaged.
PIRATE: I don't know what you mean.
PILOT: He means it's a sub. . . .
OFFICER: Yes. A war submarine.
PIRATE: Help! Help! It is sinking!
OFFICER: No, no, it's submerging.
PIRATE: I can't bear to look!
CAPTAIN: I'll grab him.
PILOT: I'll hold him.
OFFICER: I'll pin down his hands.

Now practice reading the play.

1. Choose your parts.
2. Read the play together.
3. Reread any parts that need more work.
4. Read the whole play again.
5. Check your own reading. You know the things you should do. Think about them. Are you ready to read for others? If not, practice again.
6. Read the play at the most convenient time for the class and the teacher.

THE RUNAWAY PIRATE

by Rowena Bennett

Characters

(4 men, and a narrator)

NARRATOR

PIRATE, *a rough, tough pirate who has returned to today's world and is looking for a ship*

STEAMSHIP CAPTAIN ⎤ *all talking together in the harbor when*
SUBMARINE OFFICER ⎬ *the pirate arrives. They show the pirate*
AIRPLANE PILOT ⎦ *all the things he has to learn about to-day's world.*

NARRATOR: Today's play takes us to a harbor where we find an old pirate talking to a steamship captain, a submarine officer and an airplane pilot. Let's listen in.

PIRATE: Oh, I am a pirate in search of a crew, and a nice tidy ship to go sailing in, too. I'm tough and I'm rough and there's naught I won't do for a ship and a crew . . . for some bold buccaneers with rings in their ears, and a cutlass or two. I'm tough and I'm rough and I'm used to the sea, and I want some brave boys to go sailing with me. You all look like dudes . . . but *that* fellow may do. I'll toughen him up . . . and you, sir, and you.

CAPTAIN: Are you really a pirate? A man of the sea?

OFFICER: And you want for your crew men like me?

PILOT: And like me?

PIRATE: Of course. And I'll teach you the ways of the ship.

CAPTAIN: That's kind of you, brother. We need a good tip.

PIRATE: I'll teach you to handle a rope and a sail. We'll travel so fast that we'll be out of hail by tonight . . . or tomorrow. . . .

CAPTAIN (*Chuckling*): Good gracious! What speed!

OFFICER: This kind of instruction is just what we need.

PILOT: This fellow has stepped from a picture or dream. . . .

CAPTAIN: He's not seen a smokestack, or engine, or steam.

OFFICER: Just where did you come from, my buccaneer hearty?

PILOT: From carnival? Circus?

CAPTAIN: Or masquerade party?

PIRATE (*Angrily*): You'd better not scoff in contemptuous tones. Behold the black flag with its skull and crossbones.

OFFICER: The banner that only a true pirate owns!

PIRATE: I've come from the locker of old Davy Jones.

OFFICER: The undersea locker of old Davy Jones?

PIRATE: I gave him the slip. Old Davy was sleeping. I slid from his grip and out of his keeping. I wanted a trip in a nice tidy ship.

CAPTAIN: You were really quite brave to rise from the grave.

PILOT: Perhaps we can find you a ship, noble sir.

OFFICER (*Warningly*): It won't be the kind that old pirates prefer.

CAPTAIN: There goes the *Queen Mary*. Perhaps you'd like *her*.

PIRATE: What? Is that a ship? Why! It hasn't a sail!

CAPTAIN: It travels by steam and without any gale.

OFFICER: It's a hundred times bigger out there on the seas than it looks to you now, through such glasses as these. Have a look if you please.

PIRATE: A ship run by steam? That was only a dream when I was last here. . . . Smoke! I see smoke! It's burning, I fear.

I want something small. Something tidy and neat—not a boat that's the size of an overgrown fleet.

OFFICER: Well, there's something smaller. It's painted in green with ripples of blue. . . .

PIRATE: It can barely be seen.

OFFICER: It's well camouflaged.

PIRATE (*Bewildered*): I don't know what you mean.

PILOT: He means it's a sub.

OFFICER: Yes. A war submarine.

PIRATE: Help! Help! It is sinking!

OFFICER: No, no, it's submerging.

PIRATE: I can't bear to look!

OFFICER: He'll need more than urging. We'll just *make* him look . . . where the waters are surging.

CAPTAIN: I'll grab him.

PILOT: I'll hold him.

OFFICER: I'll pin down his hands.

CAPTAIN: I'll hold up this glass, till the man understands.

PIRATE (*Breathlessly*): Look! Now it comes up! That ship is a wonder. It travels the ocean, both over and under.

OFFICER: That's what we mean when we say, "submarine."

PIRATE (*Alarmed*): But I couldn't run that ship. I just couldn't dock her. Besides she would take me to Davy Jones' locker. I've just come from there to breathe nice salty air and to find me a ship that will answer my prayer.

CAPTAIN: Very well, there will soon be another ship coming.

PILOT: There's one coming now! Don't you all hear that humming?

PIRATE: What a noise! What a scare! Another ship? Where?

PILOT: Out there! In the air!

PIRATE: What? A ship that has wings? Why! Of all the strange things! But a man such as I doesn't know how to fly. . . . And I don't think I'll try.

PILOT: Here! Where are you going? Your feet getting cold?

PIRATE: I'm a pirate, just think! I am seasoned and old with ducats that clink and earrings of gold. I'm a pirate, just think! I'm a buccaneer bold! But I'm afraid you are right. My feet have turned cold. I just couldn't navigate engines or steam, nor fly through the ether and stay on the beam. I just couldn't make any rudder behave if I had to sail *under* the billowy wave. I'm not at all brave. When I'm back with Davy I'll surely be glad. It just didn't pay to run off and be bad.

CAPTAIN: Poor fellow! He hasn't a brag or a boast left on his tongue.

OFFICER: He'll find his old post in Davy Jones' locker the thing he likes most.

PILOT (*Laughing*): He isn't a pirate. He's only a ghost.

THE END

The Runaway Balloon

This is not a fairy story but it is make-believe. Animals and children talk together. They go to strange and far-distant places. Read the play to yourself. Try to get the meaning clear. Imagine yourself in a world of make-believe.

Choose your parts.

Try reading the play together. The words and phrases are not difficult. Help one another when you need to.

1. Be sure to come in promptly with your part.
2. Read the play as many times as you need to.
3. Talk together and decide where you need to improve.
4. Practice until you feel you are ready to read for others.
5. Make arrangements with your teacher as to the best time to read for the class.

THE RUNAWAY BALLOON

by Isabel McLennan McMeekin

Characters

(2 girls, 2 boys, 1 man and the narrator)

NARRATOR

TRIXIE, *a little girl who has run away so she can play with her balloon. During most of the play she is trying to find her balloon.*

THE MONKEY, *a tiny monkey who has run away because he is tired of doing what his master tells him*

BALLOON KEEPER, *a kind man who is in charge of all the balloons that have ever been broken*

THE BIG BEAR, *who lives in the sky very close to the moon*
THE DIPPER, *who also lives in the sky near the moon. The Dipper and the Big Bear have been left in charge of the moon.*

NARRATOR: Trixie, a little girl, is in a garden. She is skipping
about, playing with her balloon and singing to herself.

TRIXIE: I went to the animal fair, and the birds and the beasts
were there, the monkey . . .

MONKEY: Good morning. Did you call me?

TRIXIE: Mercy no! I didn't expect to see a real monkey. I was
just singing. Where did you come from?

MONKEY: That's a secret. (*He whispers loudly*) I've run away.

TRIXIE: So have I!

MONKEY: Why did you run away, little girl? You have no master to make you dance when you want to sleep and sleep
when you want to dance.

TRIXIE: I have no master but I've got a grandpa and a grandma
who are just as bad. They won't let me play with my balloon 'cept just for a half-hour after lunch. I've got to sew
and practice and study and be good all day long, so I just
ran away. I came here to the park garden so I could play
and play and play with my beautiful balloon.

MONKEY: I like your balloon. I like yellow ones best of all.
Will you let me play with it?

TRIXIE: You might break it. You have such sharp little claws.
A little teeny-weeny prick, and it would all be gone.

MONKEY (*Beginning to whimper*): I want to see it. Let me see
it, please, Little Girl.

TRIXIE: My name isn't Little Girl. It's Trixie, and I won't let
you see it. So there, Mr. Runaway Monkey!

MONKEY: You're a runaway girl yourself and I will see it!

TRIXIE (*Squealing*): Oh, oh, oh! It broke! Look what you did
to my beautiful yellow balloon. You horrid little monkey. I
just hate you, yes, I do!

MONKEY: I'm very sorry. Honest I am. I didn't mean to do it.
I didn't even know my claws were that sharp. Please forgive

me, Trixie. I'll take you to Balloon Land and maybe we can get it back again.

TRIXIE (*Still sobbing*): Where's Balloon Land? I've never even heard of it.

MONKEY: There are lots of things we animals know about that you silly children have never heard of. What did you think became of all the balloons that popped? There must be a thousand every day. They've got to go somewhere!

TRIXIE: I guess they do. I've never thought of that. When can we go to Balloon Land, and what's it like?

MONKEY: I needn't bother to tell you what it's like if we're going there. We can go right now if you wish. Do just as I do and you'll be there in two shakes of a monkey's tail.

NARRATOR: Now we must go to Balloon Land. There are balloons everywhere you look. They are every size, shape and color. That is, *almost* every color. Listen to Trixie and the Monkey.

TRIXIE: Here, here, maybe it is here. Balloons, balloons, balloons, oh how beautiful!

MONKEY: All the ones that children ever lost, my dear!

TRIXIE: Red, blue, purple, green, I have never seen so many. Are they truly all the balloons that ever were?

MONKEY: I think so, but I've been away for a long while. I used to play here when I was a tiny monkey; all the little animals come here to play, tiny squirrels and puppies, little chickens and even baby elephants in their dreams. I haven't been back for a long time, and all I remembered about the place was balloons, balloons, balloons, a kind of balloon heaven.

TRIXIE: I see every color but yellow. My balloon was yellow. Why aren't there any yellow ones here? I knew I would never find mine. (*She begins to cry.*)

MONKEY: Stop! Stop! Don't cry. I'll call the Balloon Keeper and he will tell us.

TRIXIE: Oh please do. Then I won't cry.

MONKEY: Mr. Balloon Keeper, YOO-HOO!

BALLOON KEEPER: Well, well, well, young monkey, did you call me?

MONKEY: Yes, sir, this Little Girl whose name is Trixie has lost her balloon—or rather . . .

TRIXIE (*Beginning to cry again*): He broke it and I'll never find it any more. I know I won't. It's run away.

BALLOON KEEPER: Why, Little Girl Trixie, you will, I am sure. Look how many hundreds and hundreds of balloons there are all around you. Surely it is here!

TRIXIE: No, sir, it isn't. (*She is still sniffling.*) It was a yellow balloon and there isn't a single yellow balloon here. I have looked at them all.

BALLOON KEEPER: But of course there isn't a *yellow* balloon here, my child. They don't come here at all. They are needed somewhere else.

MONKEY: Where are they needed? I thought all balloons came here.

BALLOON KEEPER: No, certainly not, not yellow ones. They go to the moon. The Man in the Moon needs them to keep the moon fat. Every month it gets slim and little, only half a moon and then a lot of yellow balloons have to come to fill it up. He needs them every one and just has to have them, too. That's why yellow balloons pop sooner than any other kind. Remember that next time you buy one.

TRIXIE: Can I get it back, ever?

BALLOON KEEPER: Of course you can, Trixie, if you want it that much. You can go there right now and just take it. He won't mind, I know. He's a fine old fellow, that Man in the Moon.

MONKEY: All right, I know the way. I'll lead you straight there.

BALLOON KEEPER: Wait a minute and I'll get you a basket of lunch. It will be a long trip.

TRIXIE: Oh, how kind of you, and what a cute little basket. What's in it?

BALLOON KEEPER: Candy and fruit and cheese. All the things children like best, and now goodbye and good luck.

TRIXIE: Goodbye.

NARRATOR: Trixie and the Monkey are high in the sky. It is dark except for the stars and the moon. They look all around them. Trixie turns and speaks to the Monkey.

TRIXIE: How big the stars are and how bright!

MONKEY: The moon is round and fat tonight. I'm sure he won't miss it if we take one little balloon.

TRIXIE: I don't think we ought to until we ask. I'm sure my grandma wouldn't like me to. She'd call it stealing.

MONKEY: Well, perhaps you are right, Trixie. Monkeys aren't as particular about stealing as well-brought-up little girls are. Often I've snatched a banana or two.

TRIXIE: Well, you shouldn't have done it. Call the Man in the Moon and we will ask him.

MONKEY (*He calls loudly*): Mister Man in the Moo-oon, Mister Man in the Moo-oon!

BEAR: Did someone call the Man in the Moon? He isn't here. He had to go to earth to see about the planting of the corn so he left us in charge. I'm the Big Bear.

DIPPER: And I'm the Dipper. What can we do for you?

TRIXIE: Please, may I have my yellow balloon back? I want it so much.

MONKEY: It's my fault. I broke it and I promised she could get it back, so please, please give it to her.

BEAR: I don't know what to say. It would leave a hole in the moon and the master wouldn't like that.

DIPPER: It wouldn't look pretty at all. Now, would it?

TRIXIE (*Beginning to cry again*): I knew I wouldn't get it. Boohoo, boohoo!

MONKEY (*In an aside to* BEAR *and* DIPPER): She'll cry and cry and cry, and then it will start to rain and flood all the corn crop which has just been planted. You don't want that to happen, do you?

BEAR: No, we don't. That would be awful. When we are in charge, it simply mustn't happen. Must it, Dipper?

DIPPER: No, we can't let it. I think we'd better let her take the balloon.

TRIXIE: Goody, goody! I won't cry any more.

MONKEY: That's fine. Reach up and take it very gently and we'll see what happens.

DIPPER: Careful, please!

BEAR: Careful, please!

NARRATOR: Trixie takes her balloon. A circle comes out of the moon, leaving a large blue hole.

MONKEY: Look, it did leave an awful scar.

DIPPER: We'll have to fix it some way.

BEAR: What can we do?

MONKEY: I've got a good idea. We'll mend it with cheese. The moon is made of cheese, you know.

TRIXIE: How smart of you, Monkey. Quick, the cheese!

BEAR: That's fine. It doesn't show at all.

DIPPER: You'd never know a single bit was gone. Goodbye, little girl. Come back to see us soon again, and you too, Mister Monkey!

TRIXIE: Goodbye, and thank you all. I am so happy to get my lovely yellow balloon back again. I think I'll kiss you, Monkey, and hug you too!

THE END

SECTION THREE

Greta and the Prince

Here is another old tale. Read it through silently to get the meaning of the story.

Try this line. Change the meaning by emphasizing different words. Have different people try.

> *What* are you doing, Greta?
> What *are* you doing, Greta?
> What are *you* doing, Greta?
> What are you *doing*, Greta?

Do the same thing with this line.

> I am *sure* I look all right.
> I am sure *I* look all right.
> I am sure I *look* all right.
> *I* am sure *I* look all right.
> I am *sure I* look all right.

Let two or three girls read these lines as they think Griselda would say them:

> "I should be *ashamed* to set such humble fare before a *prince*."
> "Why *not*? It is plain to be seen that *Greta* is not *suited* to the life of a princess."

Let some of the girls read these lines as they think Greta would say them.

> "Hans, I shall be glad to bind your hand. It is a painful cut, too. Sit here and rest."
> "Can that be the Prince? Please come in! Why, it is Goodwife Anna. How are you? It is good to see you."

"Hush, Griselda! No prince is more welcome than are our friends and neighbors."

1. Choose your parts.
2. Practice reading the play.
3. Evaluate your reading:
     Could everyone be heard?
     Did everyone speak clearly and distinctly?
     Did anyone read too fast?
     Did everyone come in on time?
4. Practice again. Remember your first evaluation.
5. Plan with the teacher the best time to read the play for others.

GRETA AND THE PRINCE

by Esther Cooper

Characters

(2 girls, 2 boys, 1 woman, and the narrator)

NARRATOR

GRETA, *a quiet kind of girl. She likes people and is always willing to help them.*

GRISELDA, *proud and selfish. She does not think of anyone but herself and how she looks.*

HANS, *a poor boy who works hard tending sheep*

THE BEGGAR, *a poor hungry man who comes to ask for food. He is really the Prince in disguise.*

GOODWIFE ANNA, *an older woman who lives near the two girls*

NARRATOR: Greta, dressed in an old faded dress, is busy setting the table in a humble little cottage. Her sister, Griselda, in a lovely new gown, is sitting in the only comfortable chair watching as Greta works. Griselda speaks first.

GRISELDA (*Impatiently*): What are you doing, Greta?

GRETA: I thought the Prince might be hungry when he came, so I am preparing some food for him. It is a cold, snowy day, and he must have travelled far.

GRISELDA: The Prince is accustomed to eating fine food. (*Scornfully*) He will not care for such a meal as that!

GRETA: But it is very nice! The bread is fresh from the oven, and the butter is sweet. I have kept the milk cold, and this honey is from my own bees.

GRISELDA: I should be ashamed to set such humble fare before a prince!

GRETA: There! That must be the Prince, now!

GRISELDA: Let him come in. I am sure I look all right!

BEGGAR: I am a humble beggar, wandering over the land. The day is cold and I am hungry. May I sit by your fire and eat a bit of bread?

GRETA (*Kindly*): Of course. Won't you have this chair?

BEGGAR: No, I shall be content to sit by the fire.

GRETA: I will give you some food at once.

GRISELDA (*Angrily*): Greta, you're foolish to let a beggar come here when we are expecting the Prince!

BEGGAR: The Prince?

GRETA: Yes, the Prince is to choose a bride today. He will knock at every door in the kingdom, and the fairest maid he meets will be his wife.

GRISELDA: Greta, don't waste time talking to a beggar! Bring me my silver mirror! Someone is at the door!

GRETA: Can that be the Prince? (*Calls*) Please come in! Why, it is Goodwife Anna. How are you? It is good to see you.

GOODWIFE ANNA: I am very tired, Greta. May I rest a while in your warm cottage?

GRETA: Why, surely, Goodwife Anna! Sit here by the fire and I'll give you some food.

GOODWIFE ANNA: Thank you, my child. It is kind of you to be so thoughtful.

GRISELDA: I had hoped we would be alone when the Prince came!

GRETA: Hush, Griselda! No prince is more welcome than are our friends and neighbors!

GOODWIFE ANNA: The Prince is to choose his bride today, is he not?

GRISELDA: Yes, indeed! That is why I am wearing a new gown.

GOODWIFE ANNA: And have you no new gown, Greta?

GRETA: My sales in the market place were poor this week, and there was not enough money for two new frocks.

GOODWIFE ANNA: So you bought one for your sister?

GRETA: It is best that Griselda have the dress. I am sure the Prince would never choose me, anyway.

GOODWIFE ANNA: And why not, my child?

GRISELDA (*Haughtily*): Why *not?* It is plain to be seen that Greta is not suited for the life of a princess! She . . . I hear someone!

GRETA: This time it must be the Prince! (*Calls*) Come in! Hans! What has happened to you? Come here.

HANS: Good day, neighbors. I cut my hand on an icy ledge and I thought you'd wrap it for me. You are always so kind.

GRISELDA: Good gracious! Is everybody in the kingdom coming here for favors?

GRETA: Hans, I shall be glad to bind your hand. It is a painful cut, too. The life of a shepherd boy is hard. Sit here and rest, and let me give you some food. I'll clean and bandage the cut first.

HANS: How kind you are, Greta!

GRETA: It is nothing, Hans. I like to help people.

GRISELDA: It is growing late, and I am tired of sitting here in style. Is the Prince *never* coming? Look out the door, Greta.

BEGGAR: My friends, the Prince is here!

NARRATOR: The beggar stands. He takes off his ragged cape and places a silver crown upon his head. Everyone bows low. The Prince speaks.

PRINCE: Please rise, good people!

GRETA: You are really the Prince?

GRISELDA: Oh, Your Highness, we are greatly honored! We are *greatly* honored!

PRINCE: In this humble cottage, my search for a bride has ended.

GRISELDA: Really? Oh, Your Highness, really?

PRINCE: Greta is to be my bride.

GRISELDA (*In dismay*): *Greta?*

PRINCE: She is good and kind and will make a charming princess, whom all the kingdom will love and honor. I have seen her true self. I knew those who thought me a beggar would show their true selves and not pretend to be something they are not. That is why I came in disguise.

GOODWIFE ANNA: You are wise, my son.

HANS: You are fortunate, Your Highness!

GRETA: But, Your Highness, are you sure . . . ?

PRINCE: *Your* Highness, I am very sure! (*Merrily*) Long live the Princess!

THE END

Small Shoes and Small Tulips

Read this play through to yourselves.
How well do you say these names?

Mr. Van Dreyton
Katrinka
Gretchen
Klopenmaker
Katrinka-Rose
Gretchen Pink-Cheek

Now practice reading the play right away without any exercises. How many things do you remember about reading plays? See how many things you can list.

Now choose your parts.

1. Practice reading aloud together.
2. Go over any parts that need extra work.
3. Look back at the list you made before reading. Have you remembered all these things?
4. If you are sure you have practiced enough, prepare to read the play to the class.

SMALL SHOES AND SMALL TULIPS

by Esther MacLellan and Catherine V. Schroll

Characters

(1 woman, 2 men, 2 boys, 2 girls, and the narrator)

NARRATOR

MRS. VAN DREYTON

MR. VAN DREYTON, *who is growing a new kind of tulip*

KATRINKA, *a daughter*

GRETCHEN, *another daughter*

JAN, *a son*

GRANDFATHER VAN DREYTON

DICK, *an American visitor*

NARRATOR: We are going to Holland, the land of windmills, dikes, and wooden shoes. In a little Dutch town we'll look in on the Van Dreyton family. Grandfather Van Dreyton, Mrs. Van Dreyton and Katrinka are there. Evidently Katrinka does not like to do housework.

KATRINKA: Scrub . . . wash . . . scrub . . . wash! My hands are in water so much it's a wonder they don't have fish scales.

GRANDFATHER: Where's Jan? I need some help in the fields.

KATRINKA: He'll be back soon. He went for a bicycle ride with Dick.

GRANDFATHER: The American boy?

KATRINKA: Yes. Sit down and talk awhile, Grandfather. No, no. Over there. This side of the room is still wet.

GRANDFATHER: That's right, Katrinka. Keep the house clean like a good little Dutch girl.

KATRINKA (*Laughingly*): I'm not a good little Dutch girl. I'm lazy. If Mother sees a piece of dirt no bigger than a tulip petal, I know she will make me wash the floor again.

GRANDFATHER: Of course, my dear. The women of Holland are famous the world over for cleanliness.

KATRINKA: Before you enter, Gretchen, off with your shoes, and hop over beside Grandfather. I don't want a speck of dust on my floor.

GRETCHEN: All right.

GRANDFATHER: You children should wear wooden shoes like mine, and always take them off when you enter the house.

GRETCHEN: I'm glad I don't have to wear them. Clippety-clop. Clippety-clop. Clumsy things.

GRANDFATHER: Nonsense! Wooden shoes are cheap and sensible. They don't rot like leather ones do when you work in wet ground. I should know. Many's the pair I've made.

KATRINKA: Move, please. Now this part of the room gets a scrubbing.

GRETCHEN: I didn't know you were a klopenmaker. Didn't you always have a farm, Grandfather?

GRANDFATHER: Always, but I made shoes, too. I still make them in the long winter evenings, Gretchen, when you and Katrinka are back home again in Amsterdam. But wooden shoes are not easy to sell. Last year a shopkeeper ordered three dozen pairs of little wooden shoes. Then pfff! The man wouldn't take them. He said his customers thought wooden shoes old-fashioned.

GRETCHEN: I call that mean. What did you do with the shoes, Grandfather?

GRANDFATHER: They're in the attic. Would you like to see a pair?

KATRINKA: *I* would, Grandpa. But be careful. This way, please.

GRETCHEN: I thought Wilhelmina was coming over.

KATRINKA: She can't. Market starts next week, and she's helping her father pack cheeses.

GRETCHEN: I wish we had a place in the market as we did last year. It was so much fun to sell.

KATRINKA: Father says no one would want small tulips.

GRETCHEN: Then why didn't he grow big ones?

KATRINKA: I don't know, Gretchen. There, I've finished. Doesn't the floor look beautiful?

GRANDFATHER: It certainly does.

GRETCHEN: What sweet little shoes!

GRANDFATHER: Sweet! That's no word for shoes. Sugar's sweet.

KATRINKA: They're pretty, Grandpa. Much too pretty to be hidden away in the attic. I'll put them on the shelf. Don't they make the room look nice?

GRETCHEN: It would look nicer without a bucket and a scrubbing brush in the middle.

GRANDFATHER: Shoes on a shelf! Well!

GRETCHEN: Why can't we have a place in the market, Grand-father? Why don't people want small tulips? Why did Father grow little ones if no one likes them?

GRANDFATHER: Your father was working on two new colors, Gretchen. He didn't expect the tulips to be small. That just happened.

GRETCHEN: Have you seen the new colors?

GRANDFATHER: Yes. The first buds are in bloom this morning.

KATRINKA: Oh, Grandfather! May we see them?

GRANDFATHER: Later. They're your father's special pets, my dear. He should be the one to show them. I must go to the fields.

GRETCHEN: What do you suppose the new colors are, Ka-trinka? I hope they're shades of pink.

KATRINKA: Or rose. Rose is my favorite color. Hello, Jan.

JAN: Hello. You girls know Dick, don't you? (*Calls*) Mother! We brought you something. We're hungry!

MRS. VAN DREYTON: Flowers! How beautiful! Thank you, boys.

DICK: It seemed funny just to pick them up and walk off. At home you have to pay for flowers unless they grow in your garden or someone gives them to you.

JAN: Someone gave us these. They're for anybody who wants them.

KATRINKA: The farmers grow them for the bulbs, you see. They put the flowers beside the road so we can enjoy them.

MRS. VAN DREYTON: We Dutch love flowers, Dick.

DICK: Don't you have tulips on your farm, Mrs. Van Dreyton?

MRS. VAN DREYTON: Ours are not yet in bloom.

MR. VAN DREYTON: Ah, but they are. These are the first. How do you like the new shades?

MRS. VAN DREYTON: Lovely. They are perfect, Hans, perfect. And quite different from any other tulips.

JAN: Have you named the new colors, Father?

MR. VAN DREYTON: Katrinka-Rose.

SMALL SHOES AND SMALL TULIPS 135

KATRINKA (*Excited*): Oh, Father!

MR. VAN DREYTON: And Gretchen Pink-Cheek.

GRETCHEN (*Surprised*): Named for me? Father, it's the prettiest tulip in the whole world!

MR. VAN DREYTON: And the smallest.

GRETCHEN: I like small tulips.

KATRINKA: So do I.

MR. VAN DREYTON: Well, here's one for each of you. I wish others felt the same way.

GRETCHEN: Poor Father!

MRS. VAN DREYTON: It takes a long time to grow a new tulip. Next year will be better. We can wait. Now, boys, did you have a good ride?

DICK: We certainly did. Holland's the place for bicycles. No wonder your streets are crowded with them. You don't have to wear your legs out pumping up hills.

MRS. VAN DREYTON: Our land is very flat.

GRETCHEN: I don't see why we couldn't have a few mountains like other countries do.

DICK: Cheer up, Gretchen. Think of all your pretty canals. I'm sure Holland has more canals than any other place in the world.

JAN: Mother, we've had a long ride and we've had nothing to eat since breakfast.

MRS. VAN DREYTON: We must see that Dick has a glass of our good Dutch milk and a sandwich made with our famous Dutch cheese.

JAN (*Calling*): Don't forget! We make famous chocolate, too!

DICK: Say, I like these shoes. They're so . . . so Dutch. Makes you think of Hans Brinker and stories about Holland. I want to take some home for my sisters, but I haven't seen any small ones yet.

KATRINKA: Grandfather made them.

DICK: Small shoes and small tulips. You've everything small.

GRETCHEN: I like small shoes! I like small tulips!

DICK: So do I, Gretchen. Honest. The big tulips are fancy but they're not half as cute as your little ones. Yours are . . . well, they're dainty.

JAN: Don't mind Gretchen, Dick. She's disappointed because we aren't having a place in the market this year. All the visitors from America and England and France and the other countries come to buy, and last summer they made a fuss over Gretchen.

KATRINKA: Market's fun. I like it, too.

DICK: Haven't you anything to sell?

GRETCHEN: Father says no one wants small tulips.

KATRINKA (*Slowly*): Small shoes and small tulips. We do have something to sell. Wait . . . I'll put a tulip in the small shoe. Look! Don't you like it?

JAN: It's all right. Hello, Grandfather.

GRANDFATHER: First shoes on the shelf and now shoes with tulips in them. *Feet* belong in shoes, not flowers!

KATRINKA: But don't you see, Grandpa? The visitors will take home the tulip and plant the bulb. They'll have a little bit of Holland in their gardens.

GRETCHEN: And while the tulip's growing, they won't forget us. They'll have a Dutch shoe on the shelf.

DICK: A Dutch shoe on the shelf could be useful.

GRETCHEN: You could save your pennies in it, or fishhooks, or whatever.

DICK: I like the idea. I'll be your first customer.

KATRINKA (*Laughingly*): What will you have, sir? Katrinka-Rose or Gretchen Pink-Cheek?

DICK: Both, ma'am. Katrinka-Rose for my sister Sue, and Gretchen Pink-Cheek for my sister Pat.

GRETCHEN: You can't buy them here, you know. You must come to market.

KATRINKA: We want to show you the splendid things that have made Holland famous. Our lovely Delft china. . . .

GRETCHEN: And tiles.

JAN: Even the diamond cutters from Amsterdam are having a display.

KATRINKA: And there will be all sorts of things from our dairy farms: condensed milk, Gouda and Edam cheeses, and chocolate.

JAN: Cheese! Chocolate! Come along, Dick, let's eat!

MRS. VAN DREYTON: I've been waiting for you, boys.

GRANDFATHER: The girls have a plan for the market this year, and I think it may be a good one.

MR. VAN DREYTON: My tulip in Grandpa's shoe. Rather neat, isn't it?

KATRINKA: Small tulips in small shoes, Mother. Dick wants some, and I'm sure other people will buy them, too.

GRETCHEN: How do you like the idea, Mother?

MRS. VAN DREYTON: I like it very much, and I believe the visitors will like it, too. When our friends from other lands buy this souvenir, they truly buy a little bit of Holland.

THE END

Who Started the Fire

Read the play *Who Started the Fire*.

This play has something important to tell which has nothing to do with the Chicago fire. If you discovered the important message, tell the class what it is.

Do some practice exercises to get ready for the play. Choose two boys and two girls.

Exercise 1.

> BILL: My *grandmother* says *Bob* broke the branch off our apple tree.
>
> BOB: *I did not.*
>
> BILL: My grandmother was *there!* She *saw* you.
>
> BOB: Yes, of course she saw me. I walked in the yard and *there* was the branch. I think *Mary* and *Ellen* did it.
>
> MARY: *We* didn't break the branch, did we, Ellen?
>
> ELLEN: No, we *didn't,* and you didn't *see* us *either,* Bob.

Did your voices sound indignant, angry, accusing?

Exercise 2.

See how clearly you can say these lines. *Take turns.*

> Peter Piper picked a peck of pickled peppers. Where are those pickled peppers Peter Piper picked?

Notice how you have to use your lips, teeth and tongue. Try this one:

> The silly sailor sat on the satin sofa.
>
> Pick a daffy! Pick a dilly! Pick a daffy dilly! The maidens at the fountainhead are nodding willy nilly.
>
> Jiggity jig. Jiggety jig. Johnny Jumper is dancing a jig.

You should be ready to read after all this practice.

1. Choose your parts.
2. Read aloud together. Help each other when necessary.
3. Go back and practice again those parts that were not good.
4. Read the entire play through again.

If you are sure you are ready, have your chairman arrange a time when the class can listen to you.

WHO STARTED THE FIRE

by Catherine Urban

Characters

(3 girls, 4 boys, 1 man, and the narrator)

NARRATOR

COW, *a talking animal*

JIM
PAUL } *boys walking home from school*

SUE
LOU } *milkmaids*

BILL
WILL } *men who were playing cards on the night of the fire*

MICHAEL, *a reporter*

NARRATOR: Jim and Paul are on their way home from school. Jim has some school books with him. Paul has his ball and bat. They are stopping by a fence. Inside the fence is a cow. Let's listen to what Jim is saying.

JIM: I'd play ball with you, Paul, but I just have to go home and learn my part for the play.

PAUL: Well, I'm glad I'm not in the old thing. Seems to me we're studying or reading about fire prevention all the time! I don't know why they have to have a special week!

JIM: It's to remind people what grave damage a small fire can do. It was in October that the Chicago fire started—in 1871 —when most of that great city was destroyed.

PAUL: Well . . . who started it?

JIM: It seems that a Mrs. O'Leary kept a cow in a barn in back of her house. One night, when she was milking it, the cow kicked over a lamp that stood near by. There was hay about and so the fire spread rapidly.

PAUL: And so a whole city burned . . . all because of a clumsy cow!

COW (*Indignantly*): Why, that's an out-and-out falsehood!

JIM: For goodness sakes! A talking cow!

COW: I just won't stand by and have you make such an outrageous statement!

JIM: You mean . . . it isn't true . . . about Mrs. O'Leary's cow?

COW: Not a word of it!

PAUL: But Jim says that's the story!

COW: I can't help it! That story is definitely wrong! I guess I ought to know! (*Importantly*) That cow was my great-grandmother, many-times-removed! And goodness knows, I've heard the story often enough!

PAUL: Well, then, you tell us how it happened!

COW: Well, Mrs. O'Leary did milk my great-grandmother many-times-removed that night, but as always, she was most careful with her lamp. Even in those days, folks realized that care must be taken with all fires and lamps!

PAUL: Sure . . . but go on. How was it started?

COW: Why . . . by two silly milkmaids.

JIM: Milkmaids? Why, I've never heard anything like that!

SUE (*Indignantly*): Now, you stop right there, you ignorant cow!

LOU: The very idea! Blaming it all on us!

SUE: There's not a word of truth in that story!

LOU: Not a speck!

JIM: But how do you know? We haven't heard the cow's story yet!

SUE: Oh, we can imagine what she's going to say! We heard her start her tale. She said two milkmaids . . . and she called us silly at that!

LOU: We're the milkmaids. We did go into the barn for a bit of milk . . . but we didn't tip over the lantern!

COW: That's the way my grandmother told it to me. She said the girls did knock over the lantern!

SUE (*Vigorously*): It isn't true! Not a word of it!

PAUL: But if *you* didn't do it, and the cow didn't do it, who did?

SUE (*Surprised*): Why, the men of course!

JIM: The men?

LOU: Why, to be sure! The men who were playing cards in a little shack next door!

COW: Well! I've never heard *this* before!

BILL: Just like a couple of women! Always blaming someone else!

LOU: I'm surprised at such talk!

PAUL: So am I. Such statements never prove anything!

WILL: But she was blaming us and we never had anything to do with starting the fire!

SUE: From what I heard, you two were playing cards with some of your friends and the lamp was knocked off the table.

LOU: And in trying to put it out, you fanned the blaze so that other things in the room began to burn . . . and then the shack . . . and the barn . . . and Mrs. O'Leary's house. . . .

SUE: And the whole block . . . and the whole city. . . .

BILL (*Emphatically*): No, sir! We didn't do it!

WILL: We most certainly did not!

COW: Well, I know that my great-grandmother many-times-removed didn't!

LOU: And we didn't do it! We heard it was those men!

COW: It was the milkmaids!

JIM: It looks as if we'll never find out who started that terrible fire.

MICHAEL: That's right, lad, I don't think you ever will!

JIM: Well . . . now, who are you?

MICHAEL: I'm the reporter who wrote up the fire for my paper away back in 1871.

PAUL: Then you should know who started it all.

MICHAEL: All I know is that Mrs. O'Leary told me her cow didn't kick over the lamp!

COW: There, I told you!

MICHAEL: Mrs. O'Leary thought it was the girls!

SUE: But we didn't!

JIM: They say the men did it!

BILL: But we didn't! We always thought it was the cow!

PAUL: So you see, we'll never know.

MICHAEL: But that isn't so important.

JIM: Not important?

MICHAEL: No. The important thing is to remember that a fire started . . . and burned a whole city . . . through someone's carelessness.

PAUL (*Thoughtfully*): Oh, I get it . . . it doesn't help any to blame someone.

MICHAEL: That's right. The lesson we must all learn is never to let it happen again. To be most careful whenever we have anything to do with matches or candles or lamps.

JIM: Yes . . . to be sure that camp-fires and cigarettes are never left burning. . . .

PAUL: And that old oily rags are never left about . . . or papers or rubbish that might catch fire. . . .

JIM: To be careful when dry-cleaning. . . .

PAUL: To keep chimneys cleaned out. . . .

MICHAEL: That's right. If everyone is careful there'll never be another holocaust such as the great Chicago fire . . . and countless lives will be saved . . . as well as millions of dollars worth of property.

JIM: And that's why we have a special week called FIRE PREVENTION WEEK . . . just to make people think about it a little harder . . . to remind them to be more careful.

MICHAEL: That's right. No one wants to feel that he was the cause of great tragedy and loss to others because of a careless, thoughtless act.

COW: No, indeed!

THE END

A Kettle of Brains

Read this play to yourself in order to get the meaning and *feeling* of it.

There is nothing difficult about the words or the lines.

As soon as you have read the play decide who will take the different parts.

Now practice reading aloud together. Your big job is to see that each person comes in on time.

Betsy, Clem and the Wise Woman all get impatient with Noodle at some time or other. *Be sure you show this impatience in your voice.*

Noodle is not very bright. His speech is slow and hesitant. *Try to sound stupid as you read his lines.*

After you have read the play over two or three times decide together how well you are doing these things:

1. Does Noodle sound stupid?
2. Does Betsy sound quick, alert and confident?
3. Are your voices clear and loud enough to be heard?
4. Are you pronouncing every word carefully?
5. Is each person ready to come in with his part?
6. Are you paying attention to the punctuation?

If you can not truly say yes to these things, get busy and practice again.

Don't read the whole play. Work on the parts that are not coming right.

When you are sure you are ready to read the play for others, let your teacher know. You can then decide with her when it is best to read to the class.

A KETTLE OF BRAINS

adapted from an old folk tale
by Gweneira M. Williams

Characters

(2 boys, 1 girl, 1 woman, and the narrator)

NARRATOR

NOODLE, *a stupid boy who wants a kettleful of brains*

CLEM, *Noodle's friend who is trying to help him to get some brains*

THE WISE WOMAN, *who is old and a little impatient with Noodle. She is really poking fun at him.*

BETSY, *a smart girl who decides Noodle needs her care*

NARRATOR: Noodle, a stupid boy, is being brought to the hut of the Wise Woman. His friend, Clem, is showing him the way. Noodle is hanging back.

NOODLE (*Fearfully*): But I'm afraid.

CLEM: You want brains, don't you?

NOODLE: I need a whole kettleful, I do.

CLEM: Well, then, go to the Wise Woman's hut there and knock at the door. Maybe she knows a way to get you some brains.

NOODLE: Aw, Clem, I'm scared.

CLEM: Noodle, don't be more of a fool than you can help, will you? Go on!

NOODLE: Hello, in there!

WISE WOMAN: What do you want, fool?

NOODLE (*Hesitantly*): Well . . . well . . . well. . . .

CLEM: Noodle, you're a fool.

NOODLE (*Hopefully*): It's a fine day, isn't it?

WISE WOMAN: Maybe.

NOODLE: Maybe it'll rain, though.

WISE WOMAN: Maybe.

NOODLE (*Gulping*): Or on the other hand, maybe it won't.

WISE WOMAN: Maybe.

NOODLE: Well, I can't think of anything else to say about the weather. But, but. . . .

WISE WOMAN: Maybe.

NOODLE (*In a rush*): The crops are getting on fine, aren't they?

WISE WOMAN: Maybe.

NOODLE: The cows are getting fat.

WISE WOMAN: Maybe.

NOODLE: Wise woman, I thought maybe you could help me.

WISE WOMAN: Maybe.

NOODLE (*Desperately*): I need brains. Do you have any to sell?

WISE WOMAN: Maybe.

NOODLE: What d'you mean, maybe?

WISE WOMAN: Maybe I have and maybe I haven't. It depends on what kind of brains you want. Do you want a king's brains?

NOODLE (*Astonished*): Ooh, no!

WISE WOMAN: Or a teacher's brains?

NOODLE (*Startled*): Lawkamercy, no!

WISE WOMAN: Or a wizard's brains?

NOODLE: Heavens to Betsy, no!

WISE WOMAN: Well, what kind do you want?

NOODLE: Just ordinary brains. You see, I don't have any at all!

WISE WOMAN: Maybe I can help you.

NOODLE: Maybe? How?

WISE WOMAN: You'll have to help yourself first.

NOODLE (*Eagerly*): Oh, if I can, I will.

WISE WOMAN: You'll have to bring me the thing you love best.

NOODLE: How can I do that?

WISE WOMAN: That's not for me to say. But when you bring it here, you must answer a riddle for me, so I'll be sure you can use the brains.

NOODLE: Oh, gosh to goodness!

NARRATOR: Noodle hurried home and now we see him dragging a big bag toward the Wise Woman's hut.

NOODLE (*Eagerly*): Here it is, Wise Woman.

WISE WOMAN: Here's what?

NOODLE: The thing I love best.

WISE WOMAN: What is it?

NOODLE: My pig!

WISE WOMAN: Well, now that you're here, can you answer this riddle?

NOODLE: I'll try.

WISE WOMAN: Tell me, what runs without feet?

NOODLE (*Stupidly*): Maybe . . . caterpillars?

WISE WOMAN (*Angrily*): Idiot! You're not ready for brains! Come back again when you've decided what you love next best!

NOODLE (*Thoughtfully*): What runs without feet? . . . Gosh I loved my pig best. What do I love best after him? . . . I know! My hen, my little hen! Wait a minute, hey, wait! Just wait a minute! I'll be back in a jiffy! Wait!

WISE WOMAN: Burn, fire, burn,
       Burn to a turn,
       One thing's sure as sky and fire,
       Fools never learn!

NOODLE: Here it is! Wait, here it is! Gosh, my goodness, heavens to Betsy, wait! Don't sell that kettle of brains! Here it is!

WISE WOMAN: Here's what?

NOODLE: Here's the thing I love best next to my pig!

WISE WOMAN: What is it?

NOODLE: My hen!

WISE WOMAN: Are you ready to answer me another riddle?

NOODLE (*Bravely*): I'll try!

WISE WOMAN: Well, tell me this. What is yellow, and shining, and isn't gold?

NOODLE (*Hopefully*): Cheese, maybe?

WISE WOMAN: Fool! . . . What do you love best next to your hen?

NOODLE (*Crying*): What'll I do? What'll I do? I've lost the two things I love best! And I still haven't any brains! Whatever will I do now? They were the only two things I loved in the whole world! . . . Who are you?

NARRATOR: As Noodle looks around helplessly a girl comes in. When she sees him, this is what she says.

BETSY: Well, for heaven's sake!

NOODLE (*Still crying*): Who are you?

BETSY: My name's Betsy. What's the matter with you?

NOODLE: Oh, I wanted some brains.

BETSY: Why?

NOODLE: I don't have any.

BETSY: Well, where did you think you could get some?

NOODLE (*Sobbing*): The Wise Woman in there said she'd give me some if I brought her the things I loved best in the world.

BETSY: Well, did she?

NOODLE: No-o-o!

BETSY: You poor fool, why not?

NOODLE: I c-c-c-couldn't answer the r-r-riddles sh-sh-she asked m-me!

BETSY (*Kindly*): There, there, don't cry. Don't you have anyone to take care of you, silly?

NOODLE: No.

BETSY: No one?

NOODLE: No one.

BETSY: Well, I wouldn't mind taking care of you myself!

NOODLE: Lawkamercy!

BETSY: Well?

NOODLE: You mean . . . (*Hesitating*) *marry* me?

BETSY: Well, yes.

NOODLE: Can you cook?

BETSY: Yes.

NOODLE: Can you sew?

BETSY: Yes.

NOODLE: Can you scrub?

BETSY: Yes, I can. Will you have me?

NOODLE: Well, I guess you'd do as well as anyone else.

BETSY: That's fine.

NOODLE: But, but. . . .

BETSY: But what?

NOODLE: What shall I do about the Wise Woman?

BETSY: Let *me* talk to her!

NOODLE: Oh, no, no!

BETSY: Why not?

NOODLE: I'm afraid!

BETSY: I'm not! Don't you need brains?

NOODLE: Well, yes.

BETSY: Come on, then, come on!

WISE WOMAN: What do you want, young woman?

BETSY: Brains for my husband here!

WISE WOMAN: Your husband, eh?

BETSY: We're going to be married.

WISE WOMAN: Does he love you the best of anything in the world?

BETSY: Go on, tell her!

NOODLE: I reckon I do.

BETSY: There, now give him the brains!

WISE WOMAN: Not so fast, not so fast. He'll have to answer the riddles first.

NOODLE (*Sadly*): Oh, the riddles.

BETSY (*Unafraid*): What are they?

WISE WOMAN: What runs without feet?

NARRATOR: Betsy nudges him and whispers something. Noodle speaks.

NOODLE: Well, my goodness, water!

WISE WOMAN: H'm.

BETSY: Give him the next riddle.

WISE WOMAN: What's yellow and shining and isn't gold?

NARRATOR: Betsy whispers something to Noodle. He answers again.

NOODLE: Well, heavens to Betsy, the sun!

WISE WOMAN: H'm. Here's the third riddle. What has first no legs, then two legs, then four legs?

NARRATOR: Noodle looks at Betsy. Betsy makes swimming motions with her hands. Then she whispers something.

NOODLE (*Happily*): A tadpole!

WISE WOMAN (*Crossly*): That's right. Now go away!

NOODLE: But where is the kettleful of brains?

WISE WOMAN: You already have them.

NOODLE: Where? I can't see them.

WISE WOMAN: In your wife's head, silly. The only cure for a fool is a good wife. And you have one . . . or will have one. I can't help you any more. Be off with you! Good day!

NOODLE: Maybe she's right! . . . You'll marry me, lass? I won't have any brains if you don't.

BETSY: Of course I will! I have brains enough for two, anyway! Come on!

THE END

Snow White

This play is just a small part of the story about *Snow White*. It is very easy to read. There are no difficult words and no strange phrases.

You will have to remember to come in with your part quickly, particularly if you are one of the Dwarfs.

The Queen, who was Snow White's stepmother, is disguised as a pedlar. She is something like the witch in Hansel and Gretel.

Think of her as mean and cruel, old and ugly, with a harsh unpleasant voice that she tries to disguise. Have some of the girls try a few of the pedlar's lines:

> "Do you know, my dear, that the *girl* who wears this *ring* is *sure* to be married to a *prince?*"
>
> "Do you *know* that the *girl* who wears this *comb* in her hair will *never grow old?*"
>
> "Do you know, my dear, that if you take *even one bite* of this you will live to be *over a hundred years old?*"
>
> "Ha, ha! And you thought I was an old pedlar, eh? Ha, ha, that's rich! Ha, ha, ha, ha. . . . What is that singing? My goodness! The seven dwarfs!"

Now choose some boys to be dwarfs and practice these lines·

> 1ST DWARF: Look, there's a comb in her hair!
>
> 5TH DWARF: Someone's been here.
>
> 4TH DWARF: But who?
>
> 2ND DWARF: What's this? A *ring* on her finger.
>
> 4TH DWARF: Gold?
>
> 2ND DWARF: Cheap brass!
>
> 7TH DWARF: Our little ray of sunshine has been poisoned.
>
> 6TH DWARF: I know. It must have been the bad queen.
>
> 3RD DWARF: What queen?

Practice this rhyme all together. Work to get it smooth and clear.

> "Thou wert the fairest, Lady Queen, Snow White is
> fairest now, I ween."

You should be ready to choose your parts.
Now read the play aloud.

Think:
1. Keep your voices clear.
2. Use your voices to play the parts.
3. Be ready to come in right on time.

Work until you are ready to read the play for an audience.

SNOW WHITE

by Walter King

Characters

(1 girl, 1 woman, 8 men and the narrator)
NARRATOR
SNOW WHITE, *a beautiful little girl who lives with the dwarfs*
PEDLAR WOMAN, *a wicked woman who is really Snow White's
stepmother*
SEVEN DWARFS, *who work all day in the mines. They took
Snow White in to live with them.*
THE PRINCE, *a handsome young man who just happened to ride
through the woods at the right time*

NARRATOR: We are going to hear an episode, a part, of the story
of Snow White. This play starts as the queen, disguised as
a pedlar woman, visits Snow White in the home of the
Seven Dwarfs.
PEDLAR (*Shouting*): Fine goods for sale! Fine goods for sale!
All fit for a princess! Fine goods here!

SNOW WHITE: Oh! A pedlar! It is such a long time since anyone came selling in the woods.

PEDLAR: May I come in? I have some fine goods to show you. All alone today?

SNOW WHITE: Yes. But the seven dwarfs will be back soon. I was just setting the supper dishes.

PEDLAR (*Interested*): Really? Seven dwarfs?

SNOW WHITE (*Timidly*): Uh-huh! They work in the mines. But they will be angry if they come home and find anyone here. They told me to let no one come in.

PEDLAR: That's quite all right, my dear. I'll be a long way from here before they ever get back. See, a beautiful gold ring. Do you know, my dear, that the girl who wears this ring is sure to be married to a prince?

SNOW WHITE (*Excitedly*): To a prince! How much do you want for it?

PEDLAR: Didn't you say that the dwarfs work in the mines? Then they will have lots of money. So don't worry now about the price, my dear. The dwarfs can pay for it any time.

SNOW WHITE: Oh! Isn't it beautiful!

PEDLAR: Ah, but you haven't seen this! Now there is a real comb. Do you know that the girl who wears this comb in her hair will never grow old? She will always look as pretty as when the prince marries her.

SNOW WHITE: Can I have that, too?

PEDLAR: Certainly. Look how well it suits you, my dear. And now there is just one other thing I can spare today. And that is this great beautiful apple. Do you know, my dear, that if you take even one bite of this you will live to be over a hundred years old?

SNOW WHITE: But I dare not eat it. The dwarfs told me never to eat anything a stranger gave me.

PEDLAR: Nonsense. What are you afraid of? Bring me a knife and I will show you how delicious it is.

SNOW WHITE: Here. I have one in my hand. I was setting the table.

PEDLAR: See, I will cut it in two. There! Now you can eat that half and I will eat this. Then we'll both live to be over a hundred, eh!

NARRATOR: As soon as Snow White has taken a bite she puts her hand on her forehead and sinks down on the floor.

PEDLAR (*Chuckling*): Ah, hah, you beauty. It is all over with you now. You have eaten the poisoned half of the apple. No more will my mirror taunt me with the words:

> "Thou wert the fairest, Lady Queen,
> Snow White is fairest now, I ween."

Ha, ha! And you thought I was an old pedlar, eh? Ha, ha, that's rich! Ha, ha, ha, ha. . . . What is that singing? My goodness! (*Horrified*) The seven dwarfs! If I don't get out of here they'll skin me alive.

NARRATOR: The Queen scurries away and the dwarfs come in.

1ST DWARF: She's not here.

2ND DWARF: Not here!

1ST DWARF: Look! The front door is open!

2ND DWARF: So it is!

3RD DWARF (*Almost whispering*): She's gone!

4TH DWARF: She's left us!

5TH DWARF: What a pity!

6TH DWARF: Too bad!

7TH DWARF: Most regrettable! . . . Look here! She must have fainted!

1ST DWARF: Fainted!

2ND DWARF: Fainted!

6TH DWARF: But why?

4TH DWARF: Yes, why?

3RD DWARF: I'll listen for her heartbeat. . . . She's dead.

1ST DWARF, 2ND DWARF, 4TH DWARF: Dead?

3RD DWARF: Dead as a dead weasel.

1ST DWARF: Look, there's a comb in her hair!

5TH DWARF: Someone's been here.

4TH DWARF: But who?

2ND DWARF: What's this? A ring on her finger.

4TH DWARF: Gold?

2ND DWARF: Cheap brass!

7TH DWARF: Our little ray of sunshine has been poisoned.

6TH DWARF: I know. It must have been the bad queen.

3RD DWARF, 4TH DWARF, 5TH DWARF: What queen?

6TH DWARF: Snow White's stepmother. A hunter told me about her. She was jealous of Snow White's beauty.

1ST DWARF: What a pity!

2ND DWARF: What shall we do?

4TH DWARF: We must bury her in the woods.

5TH DWARF: But wait. We cannot lose her so soon. She must stay here for three days.

6TH DWARF: No, we cannot bury her in the black ground. She is too pretty.

7TH DWARF: I have it! Let's make a glass case and put her in that. Then we will be able to see her.

3RD DWARF: A good idea. But first we must get some flowers for her.

2ND DWARF: Snow White roses!

1ST DWARF: Any kind. She loved all the flowers.

NARRATOR: Someone is passing by the window. I can't see who it is. He is very handsome. He must be a prince.

PRINCE: Oh, I beg your pardon. I got lost in the woods. Then I saw your open door and I thought you might. . . . Why, who is SHE?

2ND DWARF (*In tears*): Our Snow White! Our dear Snow White! She has been poisoned!

PRINCE: Oh, she is beautiful! Beautiful! Like a princess! She must have eaten something.

1ST DWARF: She must have.

2ND DWARF: She certainly must have.

3RD DWARF: When we were out.

4TH DWARF: Digging.

5TH DWARF: At the mines.

6TH DWARF: We found a comb in her hair.

7TH DWARF: And a cheap brass ring on her finger.

PRINCE: These cheap things were given to gain her confidence. But she has eaten something. Look! She has something in her mouth still . . . wait! I'll remove it. . . . Here it is . . . a piece of poisoned apple! . . . Look. . . . She is coming to!

1ST DWARF (*Whispering*): So she is!

2ND DWARF: You're right, she is.

3RD DWARF: Oh, joy!

4TH DWARF: Great!

5TH DWARF: Beautiful!

6TH DWARF: Wonderful!

7TH DWARF: Marvellous!

SNOW WHITE: Where am I?

PRINCE: Here, quite safe.

SNOW WHITE: Oh, yes, I remember now. It was the old pedlar woman who did it. She gave me a poisoned apple. But . . . who are you?

PRINCE: A prince, beautiful Snow White.

SNOW WHITE: Yes, I know now. You are my prince, aren't you? The pedlar said I would marry a prince.

PRINCE (*Laughing*): Really? Then we'll go and make arrangements for the wedding this very moment.

SNOW WHITE (*Hesitating*): But . . . the dwarfs, I couldn't leave them. They took me in and sheltered me when I was lost.

PRINCE: True. And they must be rewarded for their kindness. They will come to our feast and we will visit them every week, as we pass through the woods. So, let's away.

THE END

One-Ring Circus

Read *One-Ring Circus* to yourselves as quickly as you can. While you are reading find the answers to these questions.

1. What did Kep want money for?
2. What frightened Miss Cobb?
3. Tell three tricks the mouse could do.
4. What did the children decide about Horace? Why?

Only one character needs to act differently from the boys and girls. Who is it?

What words could you use to describe her voice:

sweet—cross—haughty—bossy—excited?

Let the girls practice some of Miss Cobb's lines. Decide who does it best and why:

"I am confident they will be more than delighted to play with you while I attend the Elite Ladies' Club."

"Nonsense, Horace! You're my nephew, aren't you?"

"So! You were planning to give a common, low-brow entertainment on Cobb property without permission! Unpardonable!"

"Hurry, Horace! My smelling salts!"

"What *did* you go home for, Horace? Ooooo! Eeeee! *A mouse!* I shall *never* be the same again!"

Here are a few words that might trouble you:

Elite pronounced Ay-leet'—a superior group
pantywaist—a sissy
synthetic bucking bronco—a make-believe horse
bantam rooster—small rooster

menagerie—collection of animals
to suffocate—to be unable to breathe
to accumulate—to collect

Choose your parts.
Now practice reading the play by yourselves.
Help one another in any way you need to.
When you are ready, tell the teacher and decide on a time
to read it to the class.

ONE-RING CIRCUS

by Aileen Fisher

Characters

(5 boys, 3 girls, 1 woman, and the narrator)

NARRATOR

KEP, *a young boy who wants to be an engineer*

PINKIE, *another boy who is Kep's best friend*

SPINDLE, *who owns a pet mouse. He is a friend of Kep's and Pinkie's*

LARRY, *another one of the crowd*

JANET ⎫
CATHY ⎭ *sisters of Larry*

MIL, *their friend*

HORACE, *a very bright boy who likes to read all the time. The other boys don't care too much for him because he gets good marks and they think he's a sissy.*

MISS COBB, *Horace's aunt. She is a wealthy woman who is used to having her own way. She bosses Horace and sometimes embarrasses him.*

NARRATOR: Have you and your friends ever planned a circus to be held in someone's back yard? In a vacant lot we find Kep and Pinkie making plans for a neighborhood circus.

Kep is trying to outline a ring with sawdust. He's having a bit of trouble making it round. Let's listen to his friend Pinkie.

PINKIE (*Sighing*): Must be pretty nice to know you're going to be an engineer when you grow up. Wish *I* knew what to be.

KEP: Wait till you get through acting in this show, Pinkie. Then maybe you'll decide to be a monkey or something.

PINKIE: Thanks for the tip. Say, who's coming to the meeting?

KEP: Oh, Larry and his two sisters. They've got a stunt all worked out. Besides, Janet can turn six cartwheels in a row, and Cathy can jump rope like nobody's business. Ever see her?

PINKIE: Nope, I don't have much time for girls.

KEP: Then Spindle's going to play the mouth organ and make his pet mouse perform. That ought to bring down the house. By the way, I'm depending on your bantam rooster and your butterfly collection for the menagerie.

PINKIE: O.K. I'll bring my collection of keys.

KEP: And Mil's going to make pink lemonade and wear her clown suit and walk on stilts.

PINKIE: All at the same time?

KEP: And don't forget you're down for a trapeze act. I'll take charge of the rodeo. I'm going to engineer a synthetic bucking bronco I dare anyone to stick on more'n thirty seconds, myself included.

PINKIE (*Hesitating*): What about Horace?

KEP: Well, what *about* Horace?

PINKIE: Why don't we let Horace in on things for once? He's got more stuff than the rest of us put together. Why, his aunt's so rich she could buy out any store in town.

KEP (*Scornfully*): That old Pinch-Face.

PINKIE: And Horace could sell a lot of tickets, I bet . . . considering who his aunt is.

KEP: Nothing doing. He's a sissy. Besides, he gets too-good marks. Besides, it's a matter of principles. I don't believe in making buddies of people just to get something out of 'em.

PINKIE: He's got a Magic Set, though, and can do lots of tricks.

KEP: How do you know? You're not taking up with that pantywaist? Why, I bet he'd faint if he saw a mouse. This circus is a he-man's outfit, see? Hi, Spindle!

SPINDLE: Hi. I brought Felix so you could get a preview of his act. But look, don't anyone close down that cover tight, because it locks, and I haven't a key! Besides, it has to be left open a crack or Felix will suffocate. Here, Felix. Sit up, boy. Sit up! Naw, not down. Well, O.K. then, roll over. Atta boy!

KEP: Some mouse.

SPINDLE: He's got stage fright. Usually he minds right off. Come on, wiggle your nose, Felix. Wiggle your nose.

PINKIE: He's a circus, that's what!

KEP: Anyway, he's cute. Ought to make a big hit with the audience. Here's Larry, his sisters, and Mil. Hi, everyone! Well, now that we're all here, the meeting is called to order. As you know, we are about to embark on a very worthwhile money-making project. Not only will we entertain the neighborhood with an amazing one-ring circus, but we will accumulate a fund.

SPINDLE: We hope!

KEP: . . . . a fund, so I can go ahead with the most important experiment of my scientific career.

LARRY: Got any ideas yet about how to do it, Kep?

KEP: Well, no. Not exactly.

CATHY: Everybody I know says it can't be done.

KEP: A scientist never says "can't" . . . see? There must be some kind of defense against the atom bomb. As an engineer I won't be satisfied till I try.

JANET: Sure, it's worth a try. A circus is worth the price of admission anyway, even if you never figure out a defense.

SPINDLE: Felix says to tell you he's ready to do his stuff for the cause any time.

KEP (*Firmly*): If we charge five cents admission for children and seven cents for adults, we'd get a big enough fund so I could probably start several different experiments at once. Something ought to work . . . law of averages. Anyway, it's a worth-while idea. And there's no time to lose! Do you think we can be ready to put on the circus this coming Saturday?

PINKIE: Look! Here comes Horace with his aunt.

KEP (*Warningly*): Don't let Horace in on anything, remember. He knows too much already . . . out of books. Besides, he's an auntie's boy!

PINKIE: I bet he'd give his eye teeth to be in our circus.

SPINDLE: Let's all get in a huddle over Felix, and then we just won't *see* them.

MISS COBB: Now *there* are some children, Horace. I am confident they will be more than delighted to play with you while I attend the Elite Ladies' Club. Let me ask them.

HORACE: No, Auntie. Please don't. I believe they don't like my company very much.

MISS COBB: Nonsense, Horace! You're my nephew, aren't you?

HORACE: Just the same, Auntie . . . experience tells me. . . .

MISS COBB (*Sweetly*): Children! . . . Children!

HORACE: They seem to be rather hard of hearing. Come on, Auntie, I have an abundance of reading matter for this afternoon. I can get along by myself.

MISS COBB (*Angrily*): CHILDREN! What do you children mean . . . throwing sawdust on my lot? I could have you arrested . . . for trespassing. Do you realize it?

KEP (*Gulping*): On your lot? We didn't know it was your lot, Miss Cobb.

PINKIE: We thought a vacant lot was . . . well, vacant. You know, vacant!

MISS COBB: You did, did you? I want you to know this lot has been in the Cobb family for thirty-seven years. What do you mean . . . defiling it with sawdust? Speak up! I am positive there is a law against it.

KEP: You see, Miss Cobb, we were planning to give a circus. . . .

HORACE: How interesting.

MISS COBB: Let them explain, Horace. So! You were planning to give a common, low-brow entertainment on Cobb property without permission. Unpardonable!

JANET: It's for a good cause. Really.

CATHY: It's to earn some money so Kep can go ahead with important, world-famous experiments.

LARRY: You see, Kep's trying to figure out a defense against the atom bomb. And, of course, that takes a little money. That's why we're putting on the circus.

MISS COBB: What nonsense. I find it hard to believe that a boy of your age and appearance bothers his head about things like that.

HORACE: I think it's perfectly natural, Auntie. I have read a great deal on the subject myself. (*Wistfully*) Besides, I believe a circus might do a great deal for this neighborhood.

MISS COBB: You'd like to be in it, wouldn't you, Horace dear? Well, perhaps we might be able to arrive at a compromise. As a matter of principle I object to sawdust and circuses on Cobb property, but . . . if you will allow Horace to contribute his many talents to the success of the performance, I shall permit you the use of my lot.

KEP: As a matter of principle, Miss Cobb, we don't. . . . Hey, Spindle, watch Felix! He almost escaped. We couldn't put on the circus without Felix.

MISS COBB (*Curiously*): Felix? Are you children hiding something from me? On my own property? What do you have there. Never mind. I'll look for myself. Eeeeeeee! A mouse! A live mouse! Oooooohhhhhh! I shall *never* be the same again!

PINKIE: The lid! She banged down the lid and it locked. And Spindle hasn't got a key.

SPINDLE: Felix! He's locked in the box. He'll suffocate. Can't somebody do something?

KEP: Race home and get your collection of keys, Pinkie. Maybe one of 'em will fit.

PINKIE: I doubt it. They're mostly pretty big . . . and rusty. Horace, where are you going?

MISS COBB: A mouse! On Cobb property! Horace! Horace dear, run home this minute and get Auntie her smelling salts. That little green bottle on top of my dresser. And hurry, Horace.

KEP: Horace isn't here, Miss Cobb. He's gone.

JANET: He just ran home. And, honest, I never thought Horace could run so fast.

MISS COBB: He ran home? Ah, the dear boy thought of my smelling salts before I did. Such a thoughtful child! So considerate of his Auntie.

CATHY: Miss Cobb, do you realize what you have done? You banged the lid on poor Felix, and it locked, and there isn't any key.

SPINDLE: He's imprisoned. He'll suffocate. He was the best mouse I ever had.

MISS COBB: A mouse on my property. . . .

KEP: Maybe it *is* your property, Miss Cobb, but it's Spindle's mouse.

MIL: I bet there's a law against suffocating an innocent little person like that.

MISS COBB: Hurry, Horace. My smelling salts!

CATHY: I'd feel awful if I did it, I know that.

SPINDLE (*Mournfully*): And Felix was just getting to wiggle his nose so good. Here's Pinkie with his keys. Say, those are all too big!

LARRY: Collecting keys is a dumb hobby, Pinkie. What good are keys if they don't unlock anything?

PINKIE: Aw . . . they unlock *some* things.

JANET: Poor little Felix.

MIL: If we don't get him out soon, it'll be too late. Here's Horace back again. Say, you surely can run fast.

HORACE: Gangway! Gangway!

MISS COBB: My smelling salts. Oh, Horace, you dear thoughtful boy.

NARRATOR: Miss Cobb has her head in her hands so she doesn't see that Horace is hurrying to Felix's box. He is whipping out a piece of wire and a gadget from his cardboard box. He is working on the lock. He has opened it!

HORACE: There you are!

MISS COBB: Where, Horace? I don't see them. The little green bottle?

HORACE: What little green bottle?

MISS COBB: The one on my dresser. Do you mean to say you couldn't find it?

HORACE: Find what?

MISS COBB: My smelling salts, of course. You certainly saw the desperate condition I was in after beholding that dreadful animal. What *did* you go home for, Horace?

HORACE: Why, for my Magic Set. I've had considerable practice opening locks and undoing puzzles. That lid was nothing.

KEP: Everything's O.K. now, Miss Cobb. The show can go on. Horace saved Felix's life . . . look, he's as lively as ever!

MISS COBB: Oh, dear me. I am long past due at the meeting of the Elite Ladies' Club.

HORACE: I guess maybe I'd better be going, too. . . .

KEP: Wait a minute, Horace.

PINKIE: What's the great hurry?

KEP: I . . . we . . . I mean, we sure could use a magician in our circus. You're hot. Only we never knew it.

HORACE (*Excited*): You mean you want me to stay? Honest? Golly, I never thought I'd ever get to act in a circus! I'd like to be in on the scientific experiments, too, Kep . . . only. . . .

KEP: Only what?

HORACE: Well, I've read a great deal about atom bombs, and

what scientists say. You'd be wasting your money. There *isn't* any defense . . . all the scientists agree on that.

KEP (*Gloomily*): I've sorta come to that conclusion myself, only I hated to admit it. I kept hoping. It sounded like a swell idea to work on. (*Brightens*) But look, we could use the money for something else. We could use it in the Junior Red Cross for that National Children's Fund that helps kids in Europe and places! We could send food and things they need.

HORACE: You've solved it, Kep!

KEP: Yes?

HORACE: Sure! *That's* the real defense against the atom bomb . . . thinking about other people and doing something to help them!

MIL: You have something there, Horace. I'm for the National Children's Fund!

SPINDLE: Stand up and shake Horace's hand, Felix. He's all right!

THE END

The House Is Haunted

The characters in this play are people like yourself and your friends. Mother and Father could be your own mother and father.

To make the most of this play there should be a kind of uncertain feeling. Keep your audience wondering whether the house is haunted or not.

Use your voices to show:

excitement
fear
relief
joy

Exercise 1.

See how many different ways you can read this sentence. Make a different word important each time. Notice how it changes the meaning. Let different people try.

We were so lucky to get *anything*.
We were *so* lucky to get anything.
We were so *lucky* to get anything.
We were so lucky to *get* anything.
We were *so* lucky to get *anything*.

Now have different people try this sentence in the same way.

We *might* have to pitch a tent.
We might *have* to pitch a tent.
We might have to pitch a *tent*.

Do the same with these lines to see if you can come in right on time.

MOTHER: I've been so busy trying to fix up this house.

NORA: And you've done wonders.

MOTHER: Well, I still think sometimes it may all fall apart, but we were *so* lucky to get *anything*.

SALLY: Yes . . . remember how Dad said we might have to pitch a *tent?*

JEAN: A tent might have been fun. Not on a night like this, though. Listen to it rain.

MOTHER: I still can't understand why someone else hadn't taken this house with houses so scarce.

Check yourselves to see how well you read.

1. Did everyone come in on time?
2. Did it sound as if people were really talking?
3. Did it make sense as you listened?
4. Would it be good enough for a radio broadcast?
5. How would you work to improve it?

Choose the characters for the play.

Practice reading the play together.

Plan with your teacher the best time to read the play for the class.

THE HOUSE IS HAUNTED

by Mildred Hark and Noel McQueen

Characters

(*5 girls, 4 boys, 1 man, 1 woman and the narrator*)

NARRATOR

NORA ⎤
SALLY ⎬ *the Harris girls*
JEAN ⎦

BOB HARRIS

MOTHER

FATHER

THREE BOY GUESTS

TWO GIRL GUESTS

NARRATOR: Let's look in on a Halloween party at the Harris home. Nora, Jean and Sally Harris are working hard to get ready for the party. Mrs. Harris has just come into the living room carrying a big bowl. She speaks to her children.

MOTHER: Well, how's everything?

NORA: Oh, Mother, isn't it beginning to look like Halloween?

MOTHER: It certainly is, Nora.

SALLY: What have you got there, Mother?

MOTHER: Why, I thought if I put this on the tea table, it would look something like a witch's cauldron. We can serve the witch's brew in it.

JEAN: Witch's brew. Yum, yum. What's going to be in it?

MOTHER: Oh, a few toads' feet and a frog or two and. . . .

SALLY: Oh, Mom, I'll bet it will be hot chocolate. My, this is going to be fun. I can't wait for you to meet everyone.

NORA: The girls and boys are all so nice.

JEAN: I like this town.

SALLY: If Dad's firm had to move somewhere, I'm glad it was here. Don't you like it, Mother?

MOTHER: Well, I really haven't had much chance to find out. I've been so busy trying to fix up this house.

NORA: And you've done wonders.

MOTHER: Well, I still think sometimes it may all fall apart, but we were *so* lucky to get *anything*.

SALLY: Yes . . . remember how Dad said we might have to pitch a tent?

JEAN: A tent might have been fun. Not on a night like this, though. Listen to it rain.

MOTHER: I still can't understand why someone else didn't take this house with houses so scarce, but since they didn't. . . .

JEAN: Is it time for me to put on my witch's costume?

SALLY: Not yet, Jean.

JEAN: But I want to. I want to say charms and scare people.

MOTHER: Here, Jeanie, I'll help you.

SALLY (*Laughing*): You'll be a cute witch Jean, but you wouldn't scare anyone.

JEAN (*Disappointed*): But people are supposed to be scared on Halloween.

MOTHER: Not actually, darling. It's all in fun.

SALLY: Everyone knows there aren't really any ghosts or goblins or witches. . . . Hi, Bob.

BOB: Hi, everyone. Boy, is it raining!

SALLY: Where have you been, Bob? Nora wants you to put up crepe paper.

BOB: I've been at a meeting of that club the fellows want me to join and wait till you hear what I heard today. . . .

NORA: What's the matter, Bob? You're so excited.

BOB: You'll be excited too when you hear. You know you've all been wondering why we were lucky enough to find this house when houses are so scarce? Well, it's no wonder no one else wanted it!

NORA: We know it's old but. . . .

BOB: That isn't all. This house is . . . this house is haunted!

JEAN: A haunted house. Oh, my!

MOTHER: Bob Harris, I'm surprised at you. Where did you get such a ridiculous story?

BOB: It's not ridiculous. No one that knew about this house would live in it and that's why it was never rented.

NORA (*Scornfully*): Haunted houses! They're only in story books!

BOB: Well, this one is right here and we're living in it!

MOTHER: Nonsense.

JEAN: Maybe it *is* haunted, Mom. I'm beginning to feel kind of spooky.

MOTHER: Oh, Jeanie, you and your imagination.

JEAN: But the other night I woke up, Mother, and I heard creaking noises.

MOTHER: Old houses always creak.

SALLY: I've heard noises like that, too.

NORA: Sally, you're not actually going to believe. . . .

BOB: But I tell you, this house *is* haunted. Some old man by the name of Mr. Bockwinkle lived here for years and years and he didn't like anyone and so he swore he'd never let anyone live in his house.

NORA (*Laughing*): How's he going to stop us?

SALLY: Nora, don't say that.

BOB: And even after he died, he . . . well, he kept coming back to see if anyone was here . . . and sometimes he . . . he still does.

MOTHER: If he comes tonight he'll find lots of people.

NORA: A whole houseful!

MOTHER: Well, a haunted house for Halloween . . . what could be nicer?

BOB: You can laugh, Mother, but. . . .

JEAN (*Screams*): Ohhhhhh!

MOTHER: Jean, what's the matter?

JEAN: I heard something. Like footsteps.

MOTHER: Nonsense, dear, it's just the storm.

JEAN: But it sounded as though someone were walking about upstairs.

NORA: Jeanie, you're always letting your imagination run away with you. Didn't Mother tell you that old houses always make funny noises?

NORA: My, it's pouring. I hope the boys and girls will be able to get here.

JEAN: The lights! The lights are off!

MOTHER: Jeanie darling, it's all right. There they are on again. It's this storm.

JEAN: Maybe . . . maybe it's not the storm at all. Maybe it's old Mr. Bockwinkle.

BOB: Boy, I don't want to be in a haunted house without any lights.

MOTHER: Children, stop it. Now you're carrying this haunted house idea too far.

NORA: Of course they are. It's silly.

MOTHER: You're all just frightening yourselves . . . getting over-excited.

NORA: I hope the lights don't go out for our party, Mother.

MOTHER: They probably won't and if they do, we still have the jack-o-lanterns. We planned to use them part of the time, anyway. Oh, dear, I just thought. Some of the windows are open upstairs and the rain must be pouring in.

NORA: I'll go, Mother. I'll run up and close them.

JEAN: I feel so spooky.

SALLY: Well, stop it. You make me nervous. Bob, Nora wanted you to put some crepe paper over that lamp shade. . . . Oh, dear, there go the lights again. Mother, do you suppose they're off for good this time?

MOTHER: I'm afraid maybe they are. But we can see fairly well with the jack-o-lanterns. And there are some more candles in the desk drawer.

SALLY: I'll get them, Mother.

MOTHER: That's a good idea. And maybe I'd better call about the lights . . . maybe they can do something. I'll try, anyway.

NORA (*Calling*): Mother . . . ohhhhh, Mother!

MOTHER: Nora, what on earth. . . .

NORA: Mother, there's someone upstairs!

MOTHER: Nora, now, you're not going to start. . . .

NORA: There is, Mother. There's someone up there . . . I saw him!

BOB: It's old Mr. Bockwinkle!

JEAN: What'll we do?

MOTHER: Nora, I'm surprised at you. You've let the others frighten you. The lights went off and you probably saw a shadow.

NORA: I know the lights went off and I was scared to death.

That's when I saw him. He was shutting the window at the end of the hall. It looked as though he'd just climbed in.

SALLY: Ohhhhh! I never thought there were ghosts but. . . .

MOTHER: And there aren't. There's no ghost or anything else up there. And I'll prove it to you. I'm going up.

NORA (*Afraid*): Mother, please . . . don't go up there!

MOTHER: Of all the nonsense, Nora! When the lights went off you must have become so frightened you imagined you saw things.

NORA: But it's all dark up there!

MOTHER: There's a flashlight in the hall. I'll take that. I'll settle this once and for all.

NORA: I wish Mother wouldn't go up there. Oh dear, what can we do?

JEAN: Sally, don't keep moving away. I want to be near someone.

SALLY: I can't stand still. My teeth are chattering.

BOB: I told you this house was haunted.

NORA: I still don't believe that. . . . Mother, you are back. Are you all right?

MOTHER: Children, there *is* someone upstairs.

NORA: Mother!

MOTHER: Yes, I heard footsteps. Someone's walking around in the bedroom.

SALLY: Ohhhhhh.

MOTHER: Shh-h—let's be quiet if we can, and try not to get excited.

JEAN: Do you suppose it's old Mr. Bockwinkle?

MOTHER: Of course it isn't old Mr. Bockwinkle. It . . . it may be a burglar. I'm going to call the police. . . . Hello? . . . Hello?

NORA: Mother, what's the matter?

MOTHER: It's dead. The phone is dead.

SALLY: The wires must be down.

JEAN (*Almost crying*): Oh, Mother, what'll we do?

MOTHER: We'll have to get some of the neighbors. Bob, you

go and I'll stay here with the rest of you. . . . What's that? Those voices?

SALLY: It's the boys and girls coming to the party. I forgot all about them.

NORA: Maybe some of them can run home and get their fathers.

1ST BOY: Are we ever wet!

1ST GIRL: What a night!

1ST BOY: A good night for a Halloween party.

MOTHER: Children, I've been looking forward to meeting you all but I'm afraid we can't have any party tonight. Something's happened.

2ND BOY: What? What happened?

MOTHER: Shh, speak quietly if you can. Maybe you can help. Our lights are off. . . .

3RD BOY: But that won't matter.

MOTHER: We must do something right away. Perhaps some of you can run home and get your fathers to help us. I can't call the police because the phone's dead.

2ND GIRL: The police?

MOTHER: There's someone in our house . . . there's someone upstairs.

BOB: Maybe it's old Mr. Bockwinkle.

1ST BOY: Oh, Bob, you didn't believe all that stuff we told you! We thought it would be fun to say the house was haunted as long as we were coming here for a party . . . but that was just a Halloween joke.

BOB: Well, anyway, there's someone upstairs. Nora saw him and Mom heard him.

1ST GIRL: Listen, I . . . I think I hear something . . . footsteps!

MOTHER: If one of you will just run home and get someone to call the police. . . .

2ND GIRL: This is awful! I'm so scared I can't move.

1ST BOY: I can. I'll go.

SALLY: Listen! He . . . he's coming downstairs!

2ND GIRL: Ohhhhh. What'll we do?

MOTHER: Children, try to be calm. Stand back by the door there. You'll be all right.

NORA: But Mother, you. . . .

MOTHER: I'll just have to face him. He may be only a tramp.

2ND GIRL: Ohhhhhhhhhhhhh!

1ST GIRL: It's a ghost!

1ST BOY: It *is* a ghost!

JEAN: It's old Mr. Bockwinkle!

FATHER: Boo! Boo!

NARRATOR: Mother flashes the light on the ghost. The ghost starts to laugh and now he is throwing the sheet back.

NORA: Father . . . YOU!

BOB: Dad, what are you doing home?

SALLY: Dad, I can't believe it!

MOTHER: John, what do you mean by frightening us all this way?

FATHER: Why, I guess I did frighten you for a minute there, didn't I? But I couldn't find any dry clothes and since it was Halloween I thought it would be appropriate to come down in a sheet. I knew there'd be a party going on.

MOTHER: But we've been frightened to death. When we heard footsteps upstairs, we thought you were a burglar.

FATHER: I thought you'd be too busy with the party to hear me and I wanted to surprise you.

JEAN: But Dad, we thought you were miles away.

FATHER: I know, but I finished my business early and I did want to get here for your Halloween party.

MOTHER: But, John, how did you get in the house?

FATHER: I took a short cut from the station and came in the back way. My clothes were soaking wet. Vera, where *are* my other suits? I've looked all over.

MOTHER: Oh, dear, I sent them all to the cleaners. I thought it would be a good time while you were away. Oh, my, the lights are on. Isn't that wonderful? I won't have to mix the witch's brew by flashlight.

FATHER: But what about me? Do I have to wear this sheet all evening?

BOB: Dad, that's all right. Just what the well-dressed man ought to wear on Halloween.

MOTHER: I think you do have a clean pair of slacks, John. I'll get them.

1ST BOY: Oh, don't change, Mr. Harris . . . you make a fine ghost.

FATHER: Yes, but now that you know I'm not a real one, I think I'll be more comfortable in my slacks. I really want to enjoy this party.

3RD BOY: Boy, this is going to be a grand party all right. It certainly started out with a bang.

FATHER: It's wonderful meeting all you boys and girls.

2ND GIRL: It's fine meeting you, too, now that we know you're not a ghost or a burglar.

BOB: We even thought you were old Mr. Bockwinkle, Dad. Some of the boys told me that the house was haunted for a joke.

FATHER: Say, the only thing that's ever going to haunt this house are the good spirits . . . laughter and fun and happiness. They're going to help us have a real housewarming for Halloween, and we hope they'll stay around always.

THE END

Kitty Hawk—1903

Before you read the entire play, study these words together.

    jaunt—a short trip
    postmistress—a woman in charge of a post office
    thrust—the push or force of a propeller
    to scoop—to be the first with the news
    poppycock—empty talk, meaningless
    incline—direction or slope of the hill
    velocity—quickness or speed of the wind
    yonder—farther away but in view
    scouting around—looking around
    world's end—a part of the world that no one is interested
      in, bleak, unattractive

Read the entire play to yourself.

Decide together who would be best for each part.

Study your part. Notice whether any of the difficult words are in your part. Check to be sure you understand and can say them.

Read the play together.

Talk over the parts that need more practice.

Rate yourselves on these points:

    1. Voices were clear and easy to understand.
    2. The parts came in quickly.
    3. Voices were used to fit the part.
    4. The reading made sense to those who were listening.

Practice until you are sure you read the play well. Plan to read it to your class sometime.

KITTY HAWK—1903

by Lyda M. Ickler

Characters

(1 boy, 4 men, 1 woman and the narrator)

NARRATOR

HARRY MOORE, *a rather stupid newspaper man. He acts very bored. He is not good at deciding what might be a good story.*

JOHNNY WARD, *a young boy who lives in Kitty Hawk. He is sure that the Wrights are going to fly.*

DANIELS, *a young man from the Life Saving station. He is very interested in the Wright brothers' experiment and spends a great deal of time with them.*

MRS. PEGGLE, *an older woman who is in charge of the Post Office. She is impatient and crabby. It doesn't take very much to make her angry. She is not a friendly woman.*

ORVILLE WRIGHT

WILBUR WRIGHT

two young men who are trying to make a plane that can really fly. They are good-natured and are used to having people laugh at them.

NARRATOR: Next time you look up and see an airplane whizzing across the sky, remember that only a little over fifty years ago, people laughed at the idea of flying. Our play takes place in 1903 and is about two brothers—Orville and Wilbur Wright—who are trying to make a plane that can really fly. As the play begins, Johnny Ward is in the Post Office telling Mrs. Peggle about the Wrights.

JOHNNY (*Enthusiastic*): But I tell you, Miz Peggle, they're building a flying machine with a motor this—

MRS. PEGGLE: Now, what nonsense. For the past two years those Wright boys have been doing nothing but fooling around Kitty Hawk— And I'm told their father is a minister too.

NEWSPAPERMAN: Good morning. This the Post Office?

MRS. PEGGLE (*Stiffly*): It is—and I'm the postmistress. Mail isn't in yet.

NEWSPAPERMAN: Train's late as usual. Well, my name is Harry Moore. I'm a newspaperman covering this southern coastline —just kinda scouting around for a good scoop.

JOHNNY: Gee, mister—I know—

MRS. PEGGLE: I suppose you've made this one of your forwarding addresses, eh? Well, there's no mail for you yet. But I'll be a-saving it for you. Your name is Moore?

NEWSPAPERMAN: That's right—Harry Moore. I'll stop by in a day or two. I'm off for a trip down the coast. This section is deader than a—

JOHNNY: Say, mister—I know where you can get a swell story.

MRS. PEGGLE: Poppycock! It's only those airbirds, mister.

NEWSPAPERMAN (*Laughing*): Well now, a scoop's a scoop. What's the story, son?

JOHNNY (*Excited*): Wilbur and Orville Wright are building a real power airship over on the Kitty Hawk sand hills. They're a-gonna try it out tomorrow if there's enough wind.

NEWSPAPERMAN (*Laughs scornfully*): Is that all? Another couple of crackpots trying to be birdies, eh? Thanks, kid, but the newspapers have had enough of that hokum—Old Langley's Aerodrome flop into the Potomac finished the airship in this country.

MRS. PEGGLE: Imagine trying to fly anything in a December wind.

JOHNNY: But, mister—they've been making gliders that went up in the air swell—for three years.

NEWSPAPERMAN: Three years! Don't tell me anyone is crazy enough to spend three years in this world's end.

MRS. PEGGLE (*Angry*): I'll thank you to watch what you say about our village.

NEWSPAPERMAN: No offense, madam—I was referring only to that Kitty Hawk section.

MRS. PEGGLE: Besides, the Wright boys don't live here. They're from Dayton, Ohio—have a bicycle shop—though who runs it is more than I know.

JOHNNY: It was the government who said Kitty Hawk had the best winds for flying. If you want to go out, my Pop's launch is anchored—

NEWSPAPERMAN: No, thank you. I've got better things to do.

MRS. PEGGLE: And you should be doing something better, Johnny.

JOHNNY (*Exasperated*): But even the crew from the Kill Devil Hill Life Saving Station are helping Wil and Orv.

MRS. PEGGLE: Naturally, they have nothing better to do. Where are you going, Johnny? The mail's not here yet.

JOHNNY (*With injured dignity*): I'm going back to Kitty Hawk. Wil and Orv promised I could stay all night and help for tomorrow. You'll be sorry, Mr. Newspaperman 'cause this is gonna be a humdinger of a story. You'll see!

NARRATOR: Johnny banged the door as he left because Mr. Moore was laughing at him. He went up to Kitty Hawk and told the Wright brothers what had happened. He is talking to them now.

WILBUR (*Chuckling*): So the newspaperman doesn't think much of us, eh Johnny?

JOHNNY (*Embarrassed*): Oh, gosh—I—

ORV: That's all right, Johnny. We don't care about the newspapers. Had no intention of letting them know anyway.

JOHNNY: But didn't you invite all the folks around here like you said?

WILBUR (*Chuckling*): Yep! And five turned up. The Kill Devil Hill boys and you.

ORV: Here comes Daniels!

DANIELS: Wal, boys, your tracks all set—fer us to carry your airship up the hill?

WIL: Yep, let's go.

JOHNNY: Gosh—those tracks on the hill look like a toboggan slide I saw once.

ORV: Well, Johnny, the incline of the hill, the thrust of the propellers and the wind directly ahead of the plane will get her into the air.

WIL: But we may have difficulty keeping the machine balanced on that track before she takes the air.

DANIELS: Wal, now—can't the one of you not flying help by running alongside a-holding it level as long as it's on the ground?

ORV: A good idea.

JOHNNY: Hey—which one's going to fly her?

WIL (*Puzzled*): Gee whiz—I don't know.

ORV: I got it, Will! Let's flip a coin.

WIL: Good idea, Orv.

DANIELS: Use my coin, boys. Give me something to remember this day.

WIL: What'll it be, Orv?

ORV: Heads I win—tails you win.

JOHNNY (*Excited*): It's tails! You ride first, Wilbur.

ORV: He's right, Wil. Crawl up there now—and fly, boy, fly!

ORV (*Panting*): She's lifting! (*Faint cheer.*)

DANIELS: She's nosing!

ORV (*Frantic*): She's stalled.

JOHNNY: She's sweeping down the hillside—

NARRATOR: The airplane took off with a clatter and a roar. She seemed to lift and fly, but wait! Something has happened!

ORV (*Worried*): Wil—you all right?

WIL (*Panting*): Yep—but the machine isn't, Orv.

DANIELS: Buck up, Wil. She isn't badly damaged.

ORV (*Excited*): And she flew, Wil! She actually flew for three and a half seconds.

JOHNNY: One of her skids is broken and some of the frame work is twisted, but, gee whiz, we can fix that up in no time.

ORV: Besides, Wil, it proves that our idea for getting the plane in the air works. I'm pleased, Wil.

WIL: O.K., Orv. And now let's get her repaired right now.

ORV: Come on, Daniels—get the crew to help us get her back in the shed.

JOHNNY: How soon can the airship be ready for another flight?

WIL (*Firmly*): Let's see—this is the fourteenth. Oh—in about two or three days at the most.

JOHNNY (*Admiring*): Gee, Wil—it looks like you'll really fly a motor airship in 1903 after all. Just like Orv said you would.

WIL: You bet we will! Come on, Johnny, get those shed doors open. We've got work to do!

NARRATOR: The Wright brothers went to work to repair the damage to the airship. They have to try again, for they are sure it will fly. As they look the ship over, they talk together.

ORV: Well, there she is, Wil! As good as new and raring to fly.

WIL: Johnny just brought over a letter from Dad. He's (*Chuckling*) enclosed a dollar so we can wire him when she flies.

ORV: Well, now—that's like him. Anything from Sis?

WIL: Why, yes—here it is—a note backed on to Dad's.

ORV: What's she say?

WIL: Nothing much except she knows we're going to do it this time and (*Pause and a chuckle*) she wishes she could be here to try it herself.

ORV: Katherine's some girl! Gosh, Wil—our plane's just got to fly today. If only that blasted wind would tame down!

WIL: We can't wait longer, Orv—it's almost ten now. Wind or no wind, we'd better get the machine out and have a try at it. I've sent Johnny to signal the Kill Devil crew.

ORV: Wait 'til I get my heavy jacket. Gosh, but it's cold today —brr—

JOHNNY (*Shouting*): The crews a-coming over—right away.

WIL: Good work, Johnny. Suppose you prop those shed doors open so they don't bang on the plane.

ORV: Say, Wil, we can face the machine directly into the wind and there ought to be no trouble in getting it to rise.

WIL: It'll be hard to fly in so strong a breeze.

ORV: But look, Wil, because of the wind, the flyer's speed with relation to the ground will be low—and the landing velocity will be slow enough to make that part of it extra safe.

DANIELS: Hello, there!

JOHNNY: The crew's here. Hello, Mr. Daniels.

DANIELS: Hi, Johnny, you on hand again?

JOHNNY: Sure thing. I know Orv and Wil's a-going to fly her today. I can feel it in my bones.

DANIELS: You and Brinkley, too. He brought his camera along to snap a picture of the flight.

WIL: Where are you going to fly her from today?

ORV: How about that level spot yonder, Daniels? About a hundred feet toward the north—

DANIELS (*Shouting*): This way, men. Get the tracks out of the shed and follow me.

JOHNNY (*Apologetic*): I told everybody about today's flight, but I guess it was too cold for them to come—even that newspaperman.

WIL: That's all right, Johnny—our friends are here.

ORV: You—and the Kill Devil Crew—

JOHNNY: Well—gee!

DANIELS (*Calling*): We're ready to carry out the plane.

WIL: We're ready.

ORV: Good work! It's only ten-thirty and we're all set.

WIL: Well—Orv, it's your turn this time.

ORV: If I don't freeze to death, I'll fly her, Wil.

NARRATOR: Orv gets into the plane and starts the motor.

WIL: All set, Orv?

ORV: All set, Wil—release the wire.

JOHNNY (*Excited*): Gosh, the wind's too strong for it—she's moving slow.

DANIELS: Look at Wil—running alongside—holding her steady.

WIL (*Panting*): She's lifting—snap that picture, Brinkley— snap it now.

DANIELS: Man alive! She's climbing!

JOHNNY: She's up and down like a jumping jack! Look at her go!

WIL: She's coming down!

DANIELS: She's landed on the sand.

WIL: Orv, you did it! She was in the air twelve seconds.

JOHNNY: Oh, I knew it would happen.

DANIELS: I wouldn't a-believed it if I hadn't seen it with my own eyes. An airship lifting itself from the ground and sailing through the air!

ORV: Wil and I are going to make some more trial flights, but I wish one of you boys would run over to the post office for us.

JOHNNY (*Excitedly*): I'm headed for there right now.

WIL: Here's a dollar, Johnny. Send a telegram to Bishop Milton Wright, Dayton, Ohio. Tell Dad we flew for twelve seconds and we're going to keep working to make it twelve hours.

ORV: He sent the dollar for the telegram. He's getting to be kinda impatient—he can't wait for letters any more.

DANIELS: And I'm going back to the station and help Brinkley develop that picture he took. Hope it comes out.

WIL: Gosh—it looks like everyone's deserting us.

DANIELS: But not for long, Wil. The boys have gone to spread the news. Pretty soon you'll have rubbernecks galore.

JOHNNY: And newspapermen, too.—Just wait 'til I see a certain Mr. Moore that hangs around Miz Peggle's Post Office. Won't he kick himself!

ORV (*Laughing*): Come on, Wil, let 'em have their fun—we have work to do.

WIL: You bet! By next year, Orv, we ought to figure out enough improvements to keep this old ship up in the air for at least a minute.

ORV: And there's the speed to be checked.

NARRATOR: The Wright brothers go back to work again. They know many things about how to improve the plane. They are eager to make changes. And they are sure of one thing: someday, man will fly!

THE END

The King's Toothache

First study these words together. Be sure you can say them and know what they mean.

renowned—celebrated
proclaiming—announcing, telling everybody
populace—the people
associating—being with another person
zounds—an old word used as an exclamation
deluged—flooded
omen—sign
created—produced
circulated—spread around
occurred—happened
wedged—stuck between two objects; for example, teeth

Now try these phrases together until you can say them smoothly and easily.

obvious solution
definitely too civilized
as civilization went uphill
most logical conclusion
our toothsome morsels
on pain of imprisonment
benefit of our experience

Have someone try some of the King's lines:

"Cold water! . . . Hot water! . . . Lukewarm water!"
"Clap him in prison. Pull out my teeth, indeed. Without
    teeth how could I put teeth in my laws!"
"Of course, of course! Now let's come to the point. What
    pearls of wisdom do you have up your sleeve?"

Did he sound like a king? If not, tell what he should have done to sound the way you think a king would sound.

Let someone else try.

Have someone try the Wise Man's part:

"I am interested in learning for learning's sake. Money means nothing to me."

"You are definitely too civilized. I have it here on good authority that skulls of primitive men show teeth in excellent condition. Excellent!"

"That thought hadn't occurred to me. But I shall be glad to go into the matter, Chancellor."

Help him to improve his reading. Check his voice, his attention to punctuation, anything that would make the part better.

Choose parts for the play.

Practice reading together. After you have read it once, decide what to do next.

1. Does some special part need help?
2. Are there words you do not know?
3. Do you need to study your parts alone?

When you are ready, practice reading the whole play again. Read it over several times until you feel that it cannot be improved.

Plan to read it to the class when it is convenient.

THE KING'S TOOTHACHE

by Aileen Fisher

Characters

(1 girl, 1 boy, 12 men and the narrator)

RONNY
JUDY } two children from the United States of America

THE KING, *who is unhappy because he has a bad toothache*
THE CHANCELLOR, *who thinks he is very wise*
THE STRONG MAN ⎤
THE MAGICIAN ⎟
THE WISE MAN ⎬ *people who try to cure the King*
THE ROYAL BAKER ⎟
THREE HELPERS ⎦
THREE ATTENDANTS

NARRATOR: Once upon a time in a far country there lived a king who had everything—wealth, power, fame and devotion. Yet he had one thing too many. He had a toothache! As the play opens, the King is seated on his throne, holding his jaw in his hands. The Chancellor and three attendants wait near by. The King speaks.

KING: Cold water! Hot water! Lukewarm water!

CHANCELLOR: A splendid idea, your Majesty. A little water may be just what you need to drown the pain. You may win your own reward! If not . . . well, at this very moment the royal herald is proclaiming your message to the populace. Someone is sure to think of a remedy. Especially with a reward in the offing. I even have a suggestion to make myself, your majesty.

KING: What, Chancellor?

CHANCELLOR: If nothing else works, the court Magician may be able to pull a guinea pig out of his hat.

KING: What for?

CHANCELLOR: Why, to experiment on. You don't think it a good idea?

KING: No. I don't see what good it would be to experiment on a guinea pig. *I've* got the toothache.

CHANCELLOR: Ah . . . er . . . just as you say, your majesty.

1ST ATTENDANT: Cold water, your royal highness.

KING: Ouch! Zounds! Take it away.

2ND ATTENDANT: Hot water, your majesty.

KING: Ouch! A hundred times ouch! Take it away.

3RD ATTENDANT: Lukewarm water, your excellency.

KING: Hmmm. Not bad. Ouch! Take it away. It is all I can do to keep my head above water.

CHANCELLOR: As I was saying, perhaps if you had tried the water first on a guinea pig . . .

KING: All right, all right. Let me see your guinea pig.

CHANCELLOR: Find the court Magician and bring him here immediately, speedily, without delay, at the earliest possible moment.

ATTENDANT: Yes, honorable Chancellor.

CHANCELLOR (*Consolingly*): I feel it in my bones that by this evening everything will be all right.

KING: I wish I could feel it in my teeth.

CHANCELLOR: With the herald crying the news in every hamlet in the realm, we are bound to be deluged with remedies. One of them will be the perfect cure.

KING: I hope it hurries.

MAGICIAN (*Breathless*): Your Majesty. . . .

KING: Did you bring your hat?

MAGICIAN: That I did. A hat has a great pull for a magician.

KING: Well, see if you can find a remedy in it for my toothache. The Chancellor has suggested a guinea pig.

CHANCELLOR: Yes. I understand, Magician, that guinea pigs are becoming very scientific these days.

MAGICIAN: Oh, is that so? There are some things that I can't understand. Personally I prefer rabbits. Hocus pocus dominocus, locus crocus, get in focus. Well, I'll be. . . .

CHANCELLOR: What is it?

KING: A remedy? There is a reward, Magician, for anyone who can cure my toothache. What do you have in your hat?

MAGICIAN: Not a guinea pig, your majesty. Nor a rabbit. A . . . a . . . thin little piece of wood. That is all. (*Holds out toothpick*) I am sure it is an omen of one sort or another. Ah, I know! Something is wedged between your teeth. That is what causes the toothache.

KING: Between what teeth?

MAGICIAN: Only the ones that ache, your majesty.

KING: They all ache!

MAGICIAN: Then I suggest that you pick *all* your teeth with this little pick. It appears a toothpick is the nearest thing to curing a toothache my hat is capable of producing.

KING: Ouch! Zounds! Take your old toothpick and try it on a guinea pig! Be gone.

CHANCELLOR: That's just what I said in the first place, your majesty. Try it on a guinea pig. . . .

2ND ATTENDANT: Your royal highness, the Strong Man of the kingdom has just come into the waiting room. He says he heard the announcement of your ache and has come to propose a cure. In fact, he has thought of not one cure, but two.

CHANCELLOR: Ah, two. Now according to the law of averages, two will be much better than one.

KING: Show the Strong Man in immediately.

CHANCELLOR: I told you, your majesty!

KING: What did you tell me?

CHANCELLOR: That your teeth are all but cured already.

KING: That's what you think!

STRONG MAN: King of the realm, I have come with two suggestions. But first I suggest that you look at my teeth. Well, what did you see?

KING: The usual thing. Teeth. Perhaps somewhat bigger than most.

STRONG MAN: And stronger, your majesty! Definitely stronger. And do you know why?

KING: From associating with you, no doubt.

STRONG MAN: Not at all. Anyone can have strong teeth. It's just a question of exercise.

KING: Exercise?

CHANCELLOR: You mean running . . . jumping . . . vaulting?

STRONG MAN: I mean exercise of the teeth! Your majesty, I am afraid you do not exercise properly. You do not *chew* enough. Therefore your teeth are weak. Therefore they ache. I recommend hardtack.

KING: My dear man, I can't abide hardtack. And I am sure my teeth could never stand the strain. They would go all to pieces. Ouch! The very thought of it sends that ache jumping around again.

CHANCELLOR: The King is right. What kind of King would he be . . . to eat a tack? A hard tack. But you said you had two remedies. What is the other?

STRONG MAN: Very simple. I shall be glad to do it for you with a twist of my wrist.

KING: Do what?

STRONG MAN: Why, pull out the offending tooth, your majesty. It is, after all, the obvious solution. See. I merely fit these pliers around your tooth . . . and pull. It is soon over.

KING: No. No.

STRONG MAN: But one little tooth . . .

CHANCELLOR: That is just the trouble. It is not one little tooth. This is a jumping toothache the King suffers. Now it is here, now there. You would have to pull out *all* his teeth.

STRONG MAN: Oh. Excuse me. That is more than I bargained for.

KING (*Angrily*): Clap him in prison. Pull out my teeth, indeed. Without teeth how could I put teeth in my laws!

CHANCELLOR: I'm so happy about the guinea pig. Imagine, if the Magician had pulled one out of his hat, the Strong Man might have pulled all its teeth. Poor thing.

3RD ATTENDANT: Your majesty, the Wise Man has come. He has a big book and two pairs of glasses.

CHANCELLOR: Ah, now we are getting somewhere.

KING: Bring him in without delay.

CHANCELLOR: Courage, your majesty. Relief is in sight.

KING: What a relief that will be. I have no stomach for a toothache, Chancellor.

WISE MAN: Honored King . . .

KING: I am glad to see you, Wise Man. In fact, I can't wait. What cure have you discovered?

WISE MAN: First, there is the matter of the reward, your majesty. You see, I . . .

KING: Come, don't worry about the reward. We have plenty of money in the treasury, I assure you.

WISE MAN: What I am trying to say is . . . I am not interested in the reward. I don't want it.

CHANCELLOR (*In amazement*): You don't want it!

WISE MAN: I am interested in learning for learning's sake. Money means nothing to me. I just want to make this clear in the beginning, as a matter of principle.

KING: Of course, of course. Now let's come to the point. What pearls of wisdom do you have up your sleeve?

WISE MAN: Your majesty, it appears that you are too civilized for your own good.

KING: What's that you say?

WISE MAN: You are definitely too civilized. I have it here on good authority that skulls of primitive men show teeth in excellent condition. Excellent. Even as late as 4000 B.C. the Egyptians had strong, healthy teeth, practically free of cavities.

CHANCELLOR: What, no toothaches?

KING: The Egyptians! Come, Wise Man, let us not waste time on the Egyptians in 4000 B.C.

WISE MAN: But, your majesty, this discovery is of the utmost importance. Don't you see? It proves that as civilization went uphill, teeth started to go downhill. Yours, for instance.

KING: And what is the remedy for that, may I ask? Are you suggesting that civilized men go back to the days of the cavemen in order to get rid of their toothaches? Are you suggesting that I . . .

WISE MAN: That is more or less what I had in mind. It is the most logical conclusion I can draw from all the evidence. You will be interested in knowing, I am sure, that before the white man arrived in the Arctic the average Eskimo had broad jaws and beautiful teeth. Beautiful.

KING: You are advising me to become an Eskimo?

WISE MAN: No, no. Do not misunderstand me. A caveman would be simpler. I have gone into the subject very thoroughly, and I find that there are a number of caves available right here in your own kingdom, your majesty. Empty and waiting.

KING (*Angrily*): You can cut your wisdom teeth on this, Wise Man: Once and for all, I would rather have a toothache than live in a cave!

CHANCELLOR: There is something to what the King says. After all, caves are dark and drafty. He might get something much worse than a toothache, you know.

WISE MAN: That thought hadn't occurred to me. But I shall be glad to go into the matter, Chancellor. I might make you a report on pains that are worse than a toothache.

KING: Of all the silly ideas. Me, a caveman. No wonder he didn't want a reward! (*In pain*) Oh, oh. What am I going to do?

CHANCELLOR: Something will come along, sir, don't worry. It always does.

1ST ATTENDANT: Your majesty, the royal Baker and his three helpers are awaiting your pleasure. They have worked tooth and nail on a solution for your toothache, and they are anxious to present the fruits of their labor.

KING: Show them in.

NARRATOR: The First Attendant goes out and returns with the Royal Baker and three helpers. They carry trays of rich pastry. The King looks up as they enter.

KING: You have thought of something, Baker?

BAKER: Not only have we thought, your royal highness. We have *created*. You see, I have a theory. I believe it is your sweet-tooth acting up, craving a little pie, perhaps . . .

1ST HELPER: Cake, cookies, tarts . . .

2ND HELPER: Strudel, gingerbread, pastry . . .

3RD HELPER: Pudding, cream puffs, chocolate eclairs . . .

BAKER: If you taste our toothsome morsels, I believe you will forget all about your toothache.

CHANCELLOR: Could be, your majesty. After all, it's been a whole hour since you dipped into that box of chocolates.

KING: A whole hour!

NARRATOR: Just then there is a great commotion at the door. Ronny and Judy burst in, followed by the attendants. They run up to the Chancellor.

CHANCELLOR: Halt, in the name of the King.

RONNY: Stop, your highness. In the name of common sense, don't eat that pie.

JUDY: Don't touch that layer cake!

KING: And who are you to be giving orders to the King? Where did you come from? I have never seen the likes of you before. Who are you? How did you get here?

CHANCELLOR: Explain yourselves, on pain of imprisonment.

RONNY: Well, your honor, we come from the United States of America.

KING: Never heard of it. Did you, Chancellor?

CHANCELLOR: Never.

JUDY: Of course you didn't. Because, you see, you're way behind the times.

KING: How's that?

RONNY: You're living back in Once Upon a Time. *We're* living in the present. I tell you, we had quite a job getting way back here.

JUDY: We had to come by rocket, in reverse.

KING: In reverse?

RONNY: Yes, the rocket was geared to go backward in time instead of forward. We got the idea of coming when we read the story about your toothache.

KING: Do you mean to say there is a story about my toothache?

JUDY: Oh, yes. You can't imagine all the different stories that are published in the United States.

RONNY: Well, anyway, we got here in time, I'm glad to say.

We brought along the modern remedy for preventing tooth-ache, your honor.

JUDY: Of course, you can't expect to have good strong teeth *overnight*. Not the way you've been living.

KING: And how have I been living?

JUDY: Behind the times. Though I realize you couldn't help it.

CHANCELLOR: And you are able to bring us up to date?

RONNY: Right. It might take a while . . . so we brought our pajamas and our toothbrushes.

KING: Tooth . . . brushes?

RONNY: That's part of it. Toothbrushes. From now on you must use one after every meal.

CHANCELLOR: What a novel idea.

JUDY: Then there's the matter of vitamins.

KING: What under the sun are vitamins?

RONNY: Only one has to do with the sun, sir. Vitamin D. It's called the sunshine vitamin. You need it for good sound teeth. You need Vitamin C, too. And A.

BAKER (*Suddenly*): Excuse me, your Majesty, but I think I smell something burning in the kitchen. The royal partridge!

1ST HELPER: The royal gravy!

2ND HELPER: The royal macaroni!

3RD HELPER: The royal stuffing!

RONNY: We'll have to tell your cooks a thing or two about sweets. They're bad for the teeth. Hereafter, your honor, you must keep your sweet-tooth under lock and key.

KING: All of it?

JUDY: Most of it. You can have some sweet things . . . but not between meals. Not if you want to stay rid of your toothache.

KING: What else?

RONNY: Minerals. You'll need minerals.

CHANCELLOR: Ah, there should be no difficulty about that. Our kingdom is rich in minerals. Gold, silver, platinum . . .

RONNY: Calcium, phosphorus and iron are much more impor-tant.

KING: You don't say! When did that happen?

RONNY: Somewhere between your time and ours. You see, we are giving you all the benefit of our experience. We have a list here . . .

CHANCELLOR: Very kind of you, indeed. And do you guarantee a cure?

JUDY: We guarantee this: If you follow instructions about brushing your teeth and eating properly, and if you tell your royal subjects to do the same thing, toothaches will be a thing of the past in the entire kingdom. It's just a matter of time.

CHANCELLOR: And how can we be sure?

JUDY (*Suddenly*): You can look at our teeth as a shining example.

KING *and* CHANCELLOR (*Impressed*): They certainly are shining. And they don't ever ache?

RONNY *and* JUDY: Never.

KING: Hmmm. Since you say there is some time lag involved, I do not see how we can give you the entire reward at this time.

RONNY: Oh, we didn't come for the reward, sir. We were just sorry because you had a toothache and didn't know what to do about it.

JUDY: We just wanted to tell you some of the facts of life. We weren't thinking of a reward. But . . . look, is there a royal printer in the kingdom?

KING: Of course.

JUDY: Then instead of giving us a reward, give the money to the royal printer and have him print this list so every person in the realm can have a copy.

KING: No sooner said than done. See that copies of this are printed immediately.

1ST ATTENDANT: Yes, Your Majesty.

CHANCELLOR: Just a moment, Your Majesty. What was on that paper? We can't have just *any*thing circulated in this kingdom, you know. We have to watch our p's and q's around here.

JUDY: Don't worry, Mr. Chancellor. There weren't any p's and q's on it—just a's and c's. Just a list of foods with Vitamin A and Vitamin C.

CHANCELLOR: We can't have any dynamite on the loose in the kingdom.

RONNY: There wasn't any dynamite. Just some facts about minerals.

CHANCELLOR: We can't have anything that might cause brushes with the enemy.

JUDY: Don't worry, sir. The only brushes on that list are *tooth*brushes.

KING (*Sighing happily*): I feel it in my bones, to say nothing of my teeth, that everything is going to work out happily ever after. My friends, you can't imagine how grateful I am that you came to my rescue. Why, but for you, I might have had to become an Eskimo. Or a caveman. Imagine! A *caveman!*

THE END

Invasion from the Stratosphere

Study these words with your teacher before you go off to read the play. Some may be difficult to read, others may be easy, but their meanings may not be clear.

conquest—the act of overcoming by force of weapons
precisely—exactly, accurately
penetrate—to enter into
miscalculate—to make a mistake in planning
stratosphere—the upper part of the air surrounding the
    earth
phenomenon—an unusual event
intensity—amount of strength, force or energy
illiteracy—not able to read or write
preposterous—absurd, against common sense
emanating—sending forth
auxiliary—helping, supporting
atmosphere—mass of air surrounding the earth
fundamental—a basic or essential part
cosmic—relating to the universe

Read this play to yourselves. Look for the words you studied. Be sure you understand every line. Ask for help if you are not sure.

Have different people try these lines.

Read this as if you were a Professor. Speak clearly and with dignity:

"As for the accuracy of the report, remember, we have
been taking costly observations at ten-year intervals for
centuries."

Say this as you think a Captain would. (Remember, the Captain is talking to the Prince.):

> "We are approaching the Earth, your Excellency. At the speed we are going, we should reach the planet's atmosphere in about fifteen minutes."

Be a Prince. Be confident and dignified:

> "We aren't expecting any trouble, Captain. All our calculations are based on the last complete report of the Academy of Cosmic Sciences submitted to the Council only a few years ago."

Choose people for the parts in the play. When you have your part, take a few minutes and read it over to yourself.

Practice reading the whole play together. When you have finished, decide where you need to do more work. Some of these lines are difficult, but they must sound smooth and easy when you read aloud.

Work on different parts.

Try the whole play again.

Are you ready to read for an audience?

Get busy and make your plans.

INVASION FROM THE STRATOSPHERE

by Aileen Fisher and Olive Rabe

Characters

(5 male, 2 female; male extras and a narrator)

NARRATOR

PRINCE RAH, *from one of the planets in outer space*

TORAM, *his aide*

PRINCESS NOLA, *the sister of Prince Rah*

SIBEC, *her lady in waiting*

PROFESSOR ECKS, *a scientist who has been studying Earth for many years*

THE CAPTAIN, *in charge of the control room of the space ship*
SOLDIERS, *mechanical men who get excited every time they
hear the word "weapons"*
RADIO VOICE, *a voice broadcasting from Earth*

NARRATOR: A Prince and Princess from another planet are preparing to invade Earth. They have a professor, several as-
sistants, and some soldiers with them. They are in a large
space ship on their way to Earth. Listen! You can hear the
Prince speaking.

PRINCE (*Confidently*): By tonight we shall be rulers of the
planet Earth!

TORAM: If all goes well, Prince Rah.

PRINCE: And why shouldn't all go well? We have been preparing for this invasion for years. Once we show the way,
our other space ships will follow.

NOLA: I can't *wait* to see what those Earth People are like.

SIBEC: It seems we shan't have long to wait, Princess.

PROFESSOR: You have read the report of the Academy of Cosmic Sciences, have you not, Princess Nola? The report on
the Earth People?

NOLA: I can't believe they are as bad as the report makes out,
Professor. Always quarreling and killing. . . . Why, they
wouldn't have survived this long.

PRINCE: Don't object to the quarreling and killing, dear sister.
It plays right into our hands. I thank our cosmic stars for it.

PROFESSOR: As for the accuracy of the report, remember, we
have been taking costly observations at ten-year intervals for
centuries. It is an established fact that the people of Earth
are unable to live together in peace and friendship.

PRINCE: That makes them easy prey to our invasion. There is
no strength except where there is unity! History proves
that.

PROFESSOR: Well said, Prince Rah. As long as country is pitted
against country, hemisphere against hemisphere, the Earth

will be easy prey to our invasion. Why, with such soldiers and such weapons . . .

SOLDIERS: Victory! Victory!

PRINCE: Take it easy, men. We aren't there yet.

TORAM: With the Earth so disunited, our invasion is bound to succeed.

NOLA: Sometimes—oh, often—I think we have no right to begin this conquest of the universe.

PRINCE: Nonsense, Nola. We might as well make slaves of the Earth People and get some work out of them . . . instead of letting them kill each other off.

PROFESSOR (*Gleefully*): How they play right into our hands! Even to furnishing power for our space ship once we penetrate the atmosphere of Earth, where our regular space motors will be of little use.

NOLA: The Earth People will be furnishing power, Professor?

PROFESSOR: Precisely. It is a well-known scientific fact that fear and hatred generate a chemical substance that becomes part of the very air into which it is breathed. With the Earth People constantly exhaling fumes of fear and hate, which, I may add, are exceedingly powerful, we should have no trouble breaking through the air barrier and making a landing. For our motors have been designed to use this chemical substance for fuel as we approach the Earth.

PRINCE: In other words, Nola, the more the Earth Beings fear and hate each other, the easier it will be for us to land.

NOLA: Such strange people.

SIBEC (*Dreamily*): I wonder how it will be—to rule over another planet.

PRINCE: We'll keep the people under our thumbs, I can promise you that. Remember those stone pyramids our astronomers discovered on one of the continents? Well, those pyramids will look like toadstools compared to the monuments we'll force the Earth People to build in our honor.

NARRATOR: The Captain comes in from the motor room of the space ship and speaks to the Prince.

CAPTAIN: We are approaching the Earth, your Excellency. At the speed we are going, we should reach the planet's atmosphere in about fifteen minutes.

PRINCE: Good. I have been waiting a long time for this.

CAPTAIN: You are aware that it will be necessary to make a change-over in power when we reach the air barrier. But since the atmosphere of Earth is only a few hundred miles thick, I do not anticipate it will take long to penetrate it.

PRINCE: Only a matter of minutes, no doubt, Captain.

CAPTAIN: You still wish to skirt around the planet before making a landing, Prince Rah?

PRINCE: Yes, indeed. We will want to make a few observations. Professor Ecks has designed a powerful new telescope.

CAPTAIN: I trust it is adapted to the variations in the Earth's atmosphere. The amount of hydrogen lessens considerably, you know, the nearer we get to Earth.

PROFESSOR (*Impatiently*): Yes, yes, Captain. We have thought of everything, I assure you. And with our well-trained soldiers and our new atomic weapons . . .

SOLDIERS: Victory! Victory!

PRINCE: Yes, men. All in good time. Take it easy!

SIBEC: The word *weapons* always presses a button for them!

PRINCE: We aren't expecting any trouble, Captain. All our calculations are based on the last complete report of the Academy of Cosmic Sciences submitted to the Council only a few years ago.

CAPTAIN: As I remember, that report was based on Earth conditions at the beginning of 1945. Things may have changed since then.

PROFESSOR: My dear Captain, where is your sense of history? It takes thousands of years for fundamental changes to take place on a planet—barring unforseen collision. I assure you, the Earth People will be the same today as they were at the beginning of 1945. You must realize we couldn't make the attack sooner. It has taken all our time and thought since the last report to perfect our rockets and our weapons.

SOLDIERS: Victory! Victory!

NOLA: They certainly have been trained . . . to the last word.

PRINCE: Just be patient a little longer, men, and you will have your victory.

PROFESSOR: You can count on it that the Earth People will still be fighting and hating, Captain. Our observations indicate that Earth Man is a fighting animal. And he seems to be getting worse instead of better. At the time of the last periodic observation, the whole planet was involved in a terrific conflict.

PRINCE: Recent atomic explosions indicate that the battles may be getting even more fierce.

PROFESSOR: The chemical substance of fear and hate exhaled by the Earth People will more than power your motors, Captain, never fear.

TORAM: The Earth is a ripe plum waiting to be plucked!

SIBEC (*Smacking her lips*): Ummm . . . good!

NARRATOR: The Captain returns to the motor room. The Professor turns to his telescope, adjusts it, and speaks to the Prince. Listen.

PROFESSOR: Do you still think, Prince Rah, that the big city in the northern hemisphere, on the ocean, with all those tall thin buildings, is the best place to land?

PRINCE: It seems to me a city like that must be at the heart of things. Once it falls to us, the rest of the continent should be easy. And from all indications that continent is the arsenal of the world. Once it is in our hands, what can the other continents do? Without unity, there will be no strength to stop us. The men of Earth have not yet learned where safety lies.

TORAM: And now they won't have a chance.

NARRATOR: At this moment, the space ship gives a jolt. Everyone in the ship lurches forward. Sibec is frightened and turns to the Princess.

SIBEC: Oh, your Highness, something is the matter.

NOLA: Don't be frightened, Sibec. We are probably just entering the fringe of the Earth's atmosphere. The Captain is having to make . . . a change-over in power.

NARRATOR: There is another jolt of the space ship. Toram tries to comfort Sibec.

TORAM: There's nothing to be f-f-f-rightened about, Sibec.

PROFESSOR: Undoubtedly it's just a matter of pressure—change of pressure as we enter the blanket of air surrounding Earth.

NARRATOR: The ship lurches again, far worse than before. The Captain hurries in from the motor room and goes over to the Prince. The Captain speaks nervously.

CAPTAIN: Your Excellency, we have entered the Earth's atmosphere, but we are having difficulty . . .

PRINCE: So I notice.

CAPTAIN: . . . difficulty with the change-over. As you know, our space motors are not designed for an air blanket composed of nitrogen, oxygen, argon, and carbon dioxide. We have to switch over.

PRINCE: I know.

CAPTAIN: But we seem to have miscalculated somewhere. There is not enough power to take us through the barrier. Either that, or some new protective film encircles the Earth.

PROFESSOR: Protective film, nonsense! Not enough power, nonsense! The chemical substance of fear and hate emanating from Earth is there, Captain. Use it.

PRINCE: You have an auxiliary battery, haven't you? Why not use it until the change-over is complete?

CAPTAIN: Yes, Prince Rah. But we don't dare use the battery too long or we won't have enough power to take us back into the stratosphere again—if need be.

PROFESSOR: I fully expect we shall be able to make our landing, at any place we choose. From then on we won't have to worry about getting back into the stratosphere for a while. We'll be too busy conquering Earth.

PRINCE: Try the battery, Captain.

NARRATOR: The Captain salutes and hurries out. The Professor adjusts his telescope. He speaks as he looks through it.

PROFESSOR: That's strange. Very strange.

PRINCE: What, Professor?

PROFESSOR: I have the telescope trained on that big city with the tall thin buildings, where we expect to land. But I can hardly see the city for the wavering glow around it.

PRINCE: Glow?

NOLA: Glow?

TORAM: Glow?

SIBEC: Glow?

PROFESSOR: There's no other way to describe it. I am sure the phenomenon was not mentioned in the last report of the Academy of Cosmic Sciences.

PRINCE: Let me see, Professor. Why . . . you're right. The glow seems to vary in intensity—now brighter, now dimmer. It must be something new. I can't remember ever hearing about a glow . . . anywhere on Earth.

NARRATOR: They look through the telescope one by one. They are very puzzled. The Captain hurries in again to report.

CAPTAIN: A very strange thing has happened. Our instruments detect a radioactive force surrounding Earth like a protective film. The closer we approach, the less power we have. If this keeps up, our ship will soon be at a standstill!

PROFESSOR (*Sputtering*): Protective film! Come, Captain, you know perfectly well there was nothing about that in the report.

CAPTAIN (*Quietly*): Perhaps something has happened on Earth since the beginning of 1945.

PROFESSOR: Preposterous.

CAPTAIN: I repeat . . . our ship will soon be at a standstill.

PRINCE: Surely you can find a way through. Here, take a look through the telescope, Captain. What do you make of it?

CAPTAIN: Ah . . .

PROFESSOR: Ah . . . what?

CAPTAIN: That city seems to be the main source of the radioactivity. It is sending out forces our ship is not equipped to contend with. Just a minute. Isn't that a tall glass building at the center of the glow?

PRINCE: Yes, I believe you're right. Though at the moment the glare is so dazzling I can scarcely see.

PROFESSOR: Nothing but sunlight reflected on glass!

CAPTAIN: Listen! Our speed has been reduced to almost zero. We can't get through the barrier.

PROFESSOR: We must!

NOLA: Why don't we try the radio? Perhaps we're close enough to Earth to tune in on something.

PRINCE: Good! We should have thought of it before.

NARRATOR: The Prince turns the dials on the radio while the others lean forward and listen. The Professor speaks.

PROFESSOR: We must get through! After all the time and money we spent on our rockets. . . .

PRINCE: Sh! I'm trying to make contact.

NARRATOR: At first only a dim mumble comes over the radio. The Prince keeps adjusting the dials. Suddenly a voice comes through clearly.

VOICE: The hopes of all the peoples of the Earth are concentrated on a glass house in New York City where the United Nations is constantly at work.

PROFESSOR: What's that? United Nations? On Earth?

VOICE: Everyone can see what goes on in this glass house. For the first time in history, three-quarters of the inhabitants of the globe are united for peace.

PRINCE: United. Do you hear that? United!

VOICE: For the first time in history there is a collective effort to build a better world for all men. There is hope. . . . There is good will. . . .

CAPTAIN: We are too late.

PROFESSOR: Wait! This is just a lot of talk. Earth People have been fighting people throughout their history. They can't lose their fears and hates in a moment.

VOICE: This is the first time so many nations have united to settle international differences and outlaw war.

CAPTAIN: It is obvious from the action of our motors, Professor, that hope is becoming a stronger force on Earth than fear, that good will is now a stronger force than hate. That explains why we cannot get through the barrier.

VOICE: We support a world-wide attack . . .

PROFESSOR (*Excited*): Wait! You see. They haven't changed! They support an attack . . .

VOICE: . . . a world-wide attack on hunger, disease, illiteracy, and poverty.

PROFESSOR (*Defeated*): Captain, you are right. We are too late. We miscalculated. (*Brightens*) But we can go back to our planet and redesign the motors! We can break through somehow, with a new rocket.

PRINCE: You forget, Professor, that in union there is strength. As long as the Earth People practice what they are saying in their glass house, we are powerless. Why don't we try another planet? Mars, for instance?

NOLA: Mars!

PRINCE: What about it, Captain? Is this space ship equipped for a trip to Mars? Do you have the proper charts?

CAPTAIN: Yes, your Excellency. We have charts for all the major planets. Once we get back into the stratosphere . . .

SIBEC: Oh, I've always wanted to go to Mars!

TORAM: If at first you don't succeed, try, try again. To Mars!

PRINCE: Send a message to the rockets that are trailing us, Captain. Tell them we have decided to reverse direction, due to unforeseen circumstances.

PROFESSOR: Due to unhistorical developments!

CAPTAIN: Yes, your Excellency.

NARRATOR: The Captain returns to the control room. In a moment the space ship lurches again as it starts back.

PRINCE: Just wait till the Martians see what our soldiers can do with our new atomic weapons.

SOLDIERS: Victory! Victory!

THE END